THE REAL BOOK OF DANCE

WISE PUBLICATIONS
London/New York/Paris/Sydney/Copenhagen/Madrid/Tokyo

Contents

See following pages for Classified Index...

Classified Index

Exclusive Distributors:
Music Sales Limited
8/9 Frith Street,
London W1V 5TZ, England.

Music Sales Pty Limited
120 Rothschild Avenue,
Rosebery, NSW 2018,
Australia.

Order No. AM958960
ISBN 0-7119-8193-0
This book © Copyright 2000 by Wise Publications

Music compiled and arranged by Jack Long
Music processed by Enigma Music Production Services
Printed and bound in the USA.

Your Guarantee of Quality
As publishers, we strive to produce every book to the highest
commercial standards.
The music has been freshly engraved and the book has been carefully
designed to minimise awkward page turns and to make playing from it
a real pleasure.
Particular care has been given to specifying acid-free, neutral-sized paper
made from pulps which have not been elemental chlorine bleached. This
pulp is from farmed sustainable forests and was produced with special
regard for the environment.
Throughout, the printing and binding have been planned to ensure a
sturdy, attractive publication which should give years of enjoyment.
If your copy fails to meet our high standards, please inform us and we will
gladly replace it.

Music Sales' complete catalogue describes thousands of titles and is
available in full colour sections by subject, direct from Music Sales Limited.
Please state your areas of interest and send a cheque/postal order for
£1.50 for postage to: Music Sales Limited, Newmarket Road, Bury St.
Edmunds, Suffolk IP33 3YB.

www.musicsales.com

Ain't It Grand To Be Bloomin' Well Dead

(Old-Time - Two Step)

Words & Music by Leslie Sarony

Ain't Nobody

(Bright Disco)

Words & Music by David Wolinski

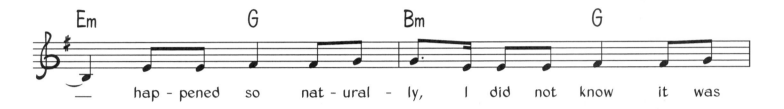

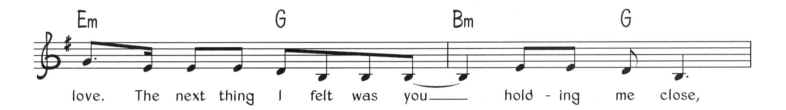

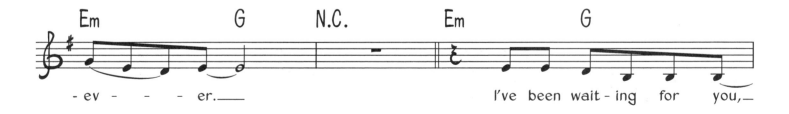

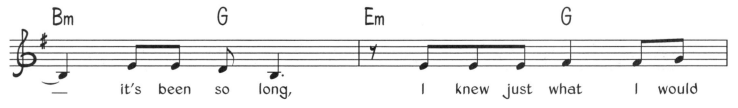

do when I heard your song,— you filled my heart with a kiss,—

— you gave me free - dom. You knew I could not re -

- sist, I need - ed some - one,— and now we're fly - ing through the

stars and hope this night will last for - ev - - er,—

huh, huh, huh, huh.— Ain't no - bo - dy— loves me bet - ter,—

makes me hap - py,— makes me feel this way.—

— Ain't no - bo - dy— loves me bet - ter,—

ain't no - bo - dy,— loves me bet - ter than you.

All The Way

(Foxtrot)

Words by Sammy Cahn ★ Music by James Van Heusen

When some-bo-dy loves you, it's no good un-less he loves you
When some-bo-dy needs you, it's no good un-less she needs you

all the way; Hap-py to be near you when you
all the way; Thro' the good or lean years, and for

need some-one to cheer you all the way. Tall-er___ than the
all the in be-tween years, come what may. Who knows_ where the

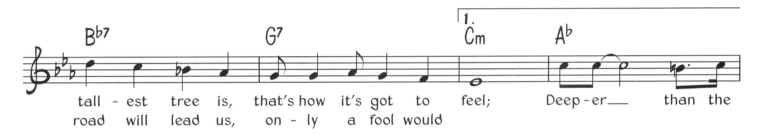

tall - est tree is, that's how it's got to feel; Deep-er___ than the
road will lead us, on - ly a fool would

deep blue sea is, That's how deep it goes,_ if it's real.

say; But if you let me love you, it's for sure I'm gon-na love you

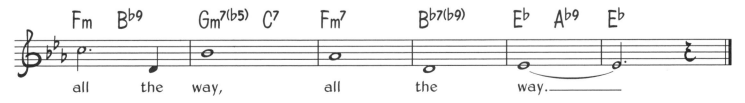

all the way, all the way.___

Angel Eyes
(Foxtrot)

Words by Earl Brent ★ Music by Matt Dennis

Amorita (Fue Mentira)
(Rumba)

Original Words & Music by Carlos Barberena ★ English Words by Len Lawson

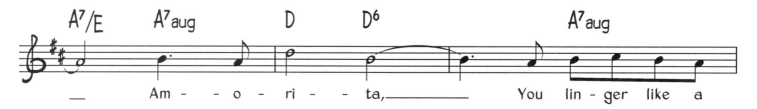

Annie Laurie
(Scottish)

Words by William Douglas ★ Music by Lady John Scott

1. Max - wel - ton braes are bon - nie, where ear - ly fa's the dew, And it's
(Verses 2, 3 see block lyric)

there that An - nie Lau - rie gie'd me her pro - mise true. Gie'd

me her pro - mise true, which ne'er for - got will be, And for

bon - nie An - nie Lau - rie, I'd lay me doon and dee. 2. Her dee.
3. Like

Verse 2
Her brow is like the snaw-drift
Her neck is like the swan
Her face it is the fairest
That e'er the sun shone on,
That e'er the sun shone on,
And dark blue is her e'e.
And for bonnie Annie Laurie
I'd lay me doon and dee.

Verse 3
Like dew on the gowan lying
Is the fa' o' her fairy feet,
And like winds in summer sighing
Her voice is low and sweet.
Her voice is low and sweet
And she's a' the world to me;
And for bonnie Annie Laurie
I'd lay me doon and dee.

Anniversary Song
(Waltz)

Words & Music by Al Jolson & Saul Chaplin

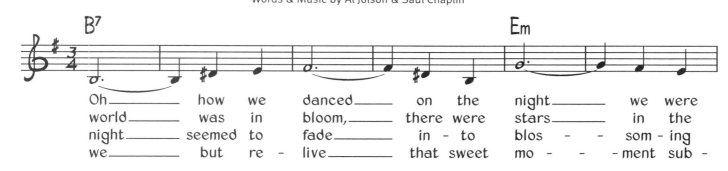

Oh____ how we danced____ on the night____ we were
world____ was in bloom,____ there were stars____ in the
night____ seemed to fade____ in - to blos - - som - ing
we____ but re - live____ that sweet mo - - -ment sub -

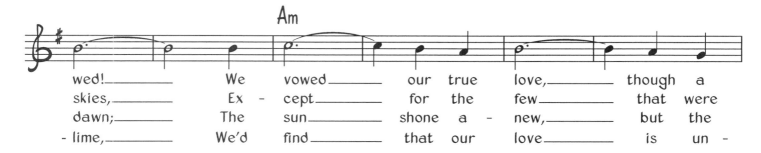

wed!____ We vowed____ our true love,____ though a
skies,____ Ex - cept____ for the few____ that were
dawn;____ The sun____ shone a - new,____ but the
- lime,____ We'd find____ that our love____ is un -

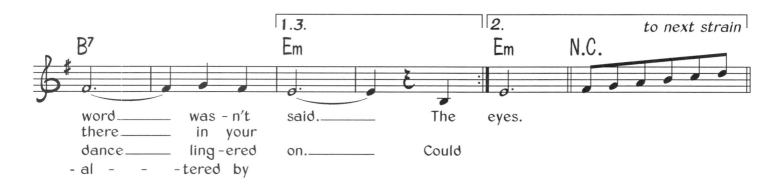

word____ was - n't said.____ The eyes.
there____ in your
dance____ ling - ered on.____ Could
- al - - -tered by

time.____ Dear, as I held you so close in my arms,

An - gels were sing - ing a hymn to your charms; Two hearts, gent - ly beat - ing, were

mur - mur - ing low: "My dar - ling, I love you so".____ The

Aranjuez, Mon Amour
(Slow Rumba)

Words by Hal Shaper ★ Music by Joaquin Rodrigo

Mon a - mour,_____ All the years__ that I have spent with you,_____

__ Were they a dream made sweet - er by your smile?__ All of the days I think of

now, Wond -'ring when__ will I see you a - gain.__

Mon a - mour,_____ All my life__ I was a - ware of these things.__

__ Of all the joy and hap-pi-ness__ with you And all the love I think of

now, Wond -'ring when__ will I see you a - gain.__

As Long As He Needs Me

(Slow Foxtrot)

Words & Music by Lionel Bart

At The Hop
(Twist)

Words & Music by Arthur Singer, John Medora & David White

Auld Lang Syne
(Scottish)

Traditional ★ Words by Robert Burns

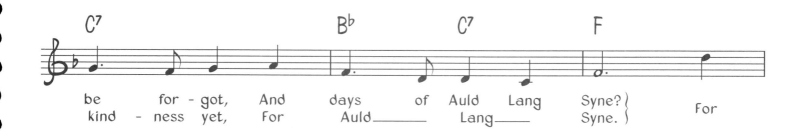

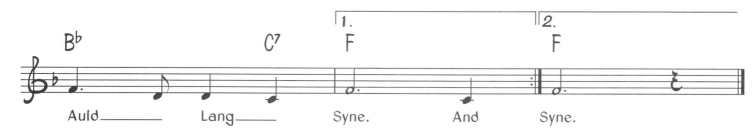

Ay Cosita Linda
(Cha-Cha)

Words & Music by Pacho Galan

On fire,— You've set— my two lips on fire,— Of your—

— kiss I'll nev - er tire,— To you— I will al - ways say Ay! Co - si - ta Lin -

- da, ma-ma! You thrill me, Like no - bo - dy else can thrill me, With sweet

— ec -sta-sy you fill me, I'll love— hon-our and o - bey, Ay! Co-si-ta Lin -

- da, ma-ma! To - ge -ther, Let's dance to the mer - e - cum-bé, The rhy -

- thm will make our hearts gay, For you— are my shin -ing star, Ay! Co - si - ta Lin -

- da, ma-ma! For ev - er may our— love go on for ev - er, Please say—

— you will leave me nev - er, Tell me— that I'm your pa -

- pa, Ay! Co -si - ta Lin - da - da, ma-ma!—

The Band Played On
(Old-Time Waltz)

Words by John Palmer ★ Music by Charles Ward

Cas - ey would waltz with the straw - ber - ry blonde, and the

band play'd on_____ He'd glide 'cross the

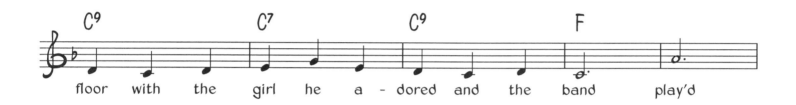

floor with the girl he a - dored and the band play'd

on But his brain was so load - ed, it near - ly ex -

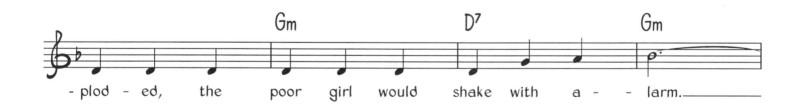

- plod - ed, the poor girl would shake with a - larm._____

_____ He'd ne'er leave the girl with the straw - ber - ry

curls, and the band play'd on._____

Baia
(Rumba)

Original Words & Music by Ary Barroso ★ English Words by Ray Gilbert

Beautiful Dreamer
(Old-Time)

Words & Music by Stephen Foster

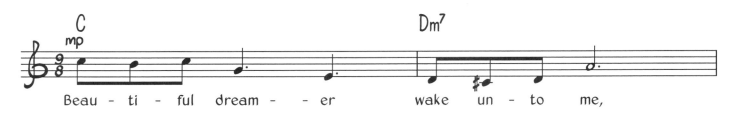

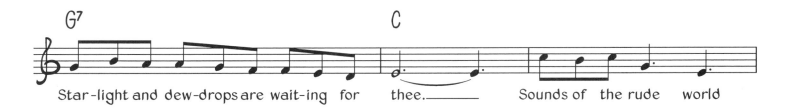

Beau - ti - ful dream - - er wake un - to me,

Star-light and dew-drops are wait-ing for thee._____ Sounds of the rude world

heard in the day, Lull'd by the moon-light have all passed a -

- way._____ Beau - ti - ful dream - er, Queen of my song,

list while I woo thee with soft me - lo - dy; Gone are the cares of

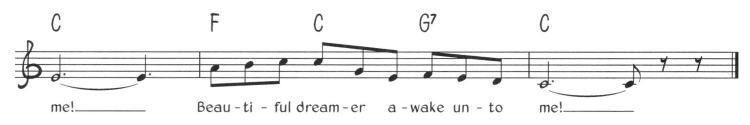

life's bu - sy throng, Beau - ti - ful dream - er a - wake un - to

me!_____ Beau - ti - ful dream-er a - wake un - to me!

Because Of You
(Foxtrot)

Words by Arthur Hammerstein ★ Music by Dudley Wilkinson

Be - cause of you there's a song in my heart.____
you my ro - mance had its start.____

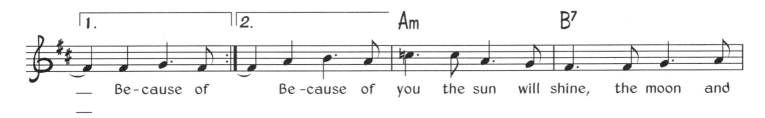

____ Be-cause of | Be -cause of you the sun will shine, the moon and
____

stars will say you're mine for - ev - er and nev - er to

part. I on - ly live for your love and your

kiss.____ It's pa - ra - dise to be near you like

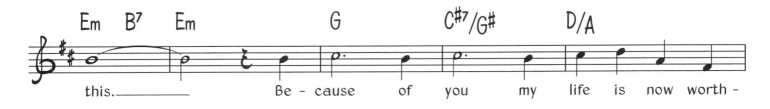

this.____ Be - cause of you my life is now worth -

- while; and I can smile, be - cause of you.____

Beyond The Blue Horizon
(Quickstep)

Words & Music by Leo Robin, Richard Whiting & W. Franke Harling

Be - yond the blue ho - ri - zon waits a

beau - ti - ful day. _____ Good - bye to things that bore

me! Joy is wait - ing for me. I see a

new ho - ri - - zon. My life has on - ly be - gun. ___

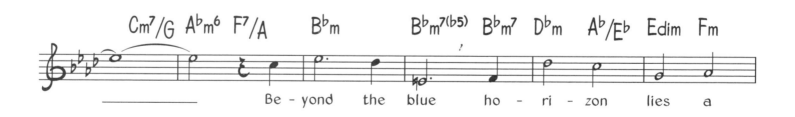

Be - yond the blue ho - ri - zon lies a

ri - - sing sun. ___ Be - sun. ___

Bless You (For Being An Angel)

(Foxtrot)

Words & Music by Eddie Lane & Don Baker

Blue Velvet
(Foxtrot)

Words & Music by Bernie Wayne & Lee Morris

The Bluebells Of Scotland

(Gay Gordons)

Traditional

Oh where and oh where is your_ High-land lad-die
(Verses 2, 3, 4 see block lyric)

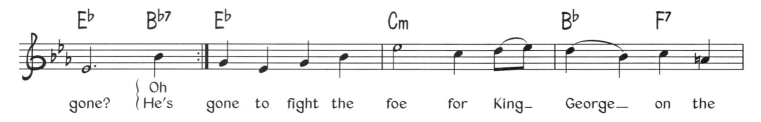

gone? { Oh He's gone to fight the foe for King_ George_ on the

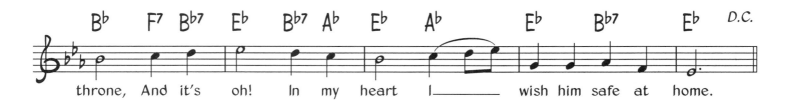

throne, And it's oh! In my heart I_____ wish him safe at home.

Verse 2
Oh where and oh where did your Highland laddie dwell?
Oh where and oh where did your Highland laddie dwell?
He dwelt in merry Scotland, at the sign of the Blue Bell,
And it's oh! In my heart I love my laddie well.

Verse 3
Oh how, tell me how, is your Highland laddie clad?
Oh how, tell me how, is your Highland laddie clad?
His bonnet's of the Saxon green, his waistcoat of the plaid;
And it's oh! In my heart that I love my Highland lad.

Verse 4
Suppose, oh suppose, that your Highland lad should die!
Suppose, oh suppose, that your Highland lad should die!
The bagpipes should play o'er him and I'd lay me down and cry,
But it's oh! In my heart that I feel he will not die.

Bo Diddley

(Rock 'N' Roll)

Words & Music by Eugene McDaniels

Bo Did - dley 'll buy ba - by a dia - mond ring.

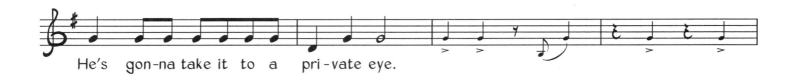

If that dia - mond ring don't shine,—

He's gon - na take it to a pri - vate eye.

If that pri - vate eye can't see,

He bet - ter not take that ring from me.

Bo Did - dl-ey caught a nan - ny goat,— To

make his pret - ty ba - by a Sun - day coat.—

Bo Did-dl-ey caught a bear cat, To

make his pret-ty ba-by a Sun-day hat.—

(Instrumental)

Won't you come to my house and rack that bone?—
Look at that— bo-do, oh where's he been?—

Take— my ba-by all the way from home.
Up to your house— and— gone a-gain!

Bo Did-dl-ey, Bo Did-dl-ey have you heard? My

— pret-ty ba-by said she was a bird!

Boiled Beef And Carrots
(Old-Time)

Words & Music by Charles Collins & Fred Murray

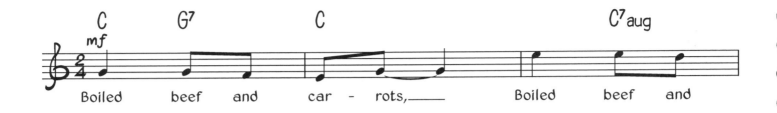

Boiled beef and car - rots,___ Boiled beef and

car - rots.___ That's the stuff for your 'Dar - by Kel.'

Makes you fat and it keeps you well. Don't live like ve - ge -

-ta - ri - ans on food they give to par - rots,___ From

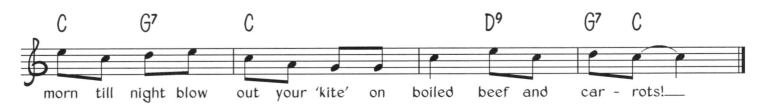

morn till night blow out your 'kite' on boiled beef and car - rots!___

Bony Moronie
(Rock 'N' Roll)

Words & Music by Larry Williams

I got a gal named Bo-ny Mo-ro - nie,

(Verses 2, 3 see block lyric)

(Instrumental)

she's as skin-ny as a stick of ma-ca-ro - ni.

See her rock 'n' roll_ with her blue jeans on,_

got no_ fat, just skin and bone._

I love her,_____ she loves me;_ oh, how hap - py we will be,_ mak-in'

love un-der-neath the_ ap-ple tree.

Verse 2
Well, I told her mama and her papa too
Just exactly what we're gonna do.
We're gonna marry one night in June,
Rock 'n' roll by the light of the silvery moon.
I love her, she loves me, *etc.*

Verse 3
She's my one and only, she's my heart's desire.
She's a real upsetter, she's a real live wire.
Everbody turns when my baby goes by;
She's somethin' to see, she really catches the eye.
I love her, she loves me, *etc.*

Brazil
(Samba)

Words by Sidney Russell ★ Music by Ary Barroso

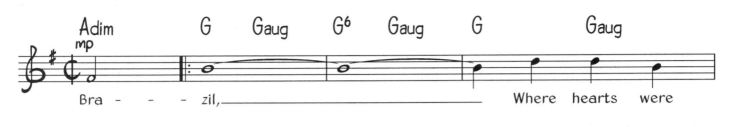

Bra - - - zil,_____ Where hearts were

en - ter - tain - ing June,_____ We stood be -

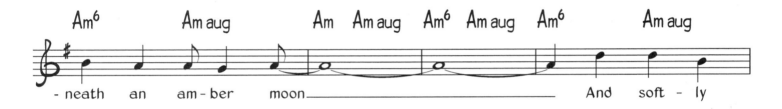

- neath an am - ber moon_____ And soft - ly

mur - mur'd "Some - day soon."_____ We kissed_____ and

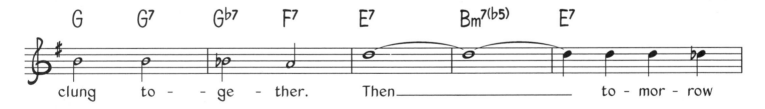

clung to - ge - ther. Then_____ to - mor - row

was a - no - ther day:_____ The morn - ing

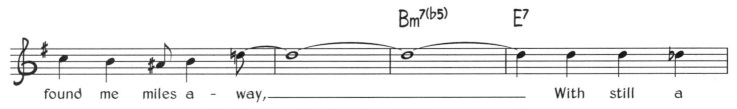

found me miles a - way,_____ With still a

Brazilian Love Song

(Baiaõ)

Words by Breno Ferreira, Nat 'King' Cole, Dick Manning & Al Hoffman ★ Music by Breno Ferreira

I see a lit-tle bird that is sit-tin' in the tree-top, A pret-ty lit-tle

bird that is sit-tin' in the tree-top, I see a lit-tle bird that is sit-tin' in the

tree-top, A pret-ty lit-tle bird that is sit-tin' in the tree-top, I see a lit-tle

bird that is sit-tin' in the tree-top, A pret-ty lit-tle bird that is sit-tin' in the

tree-top, I see a lit-tle bird that is sit-tin' in the tree-top, A pret-ty lit-tle

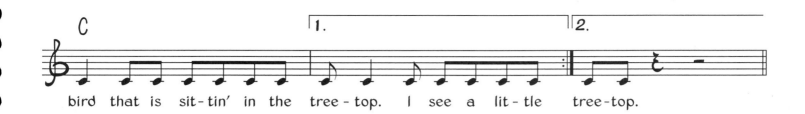

bird that is sit-tin' in the tree-top. **1.** I see a lit-tle tree-top. **2.**

Fly!_____ my Bra - zil - ian love bird,_____

Fly!_____ to the one I love._____

Please_____ won't you tell her that I'm the one who cares,

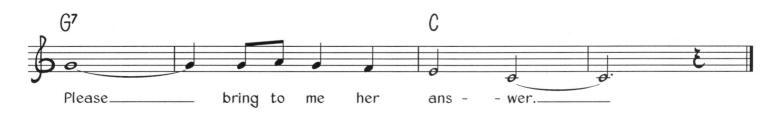

Please_____ bring to me her ans - - wer._____

Burlington Bertie From Bow
(Old-Time Waltz)

Words & Music by William Hargreaves

Moderately

I'm Bert, P'raps you've heard of me, Bert, You've had word of me, Jog-ging a-long, Heart-y and strong, Liv-ing on plates of fresh air. I dress up in fash-ion, And when I am feel-ing de-pressed, I shave from my cuff all the whis-kers and fluff, Stick my hat on and tod-dle up West! I'm Bur-ling-ton Ber-tie, I

rise at ten thir - ty and saun - ter a - long like a toff,_____

— I walk down the Strand with my gloves on my hand, Then I

walk down a - gain with them off,_____ I'm all airs and

gra - ces, Cor - rect ea - sy pa - ces, With - out food so long I've for -

- got where my face is; I'm Bert, Bert, I have - n't a

shirt, But my peo - ple are well off you know,_____ Near - ly

ev - 'ry - one knows me, From Smith to Lord Rose - b'ry. I'm

Bur - ling - ton Ber - tie from Bow!_____

Buttons And Bows
(Quickstep)

Words & Music by Jay Livingston & Ray Evans

East is east and west is west, and the wrong one I have chose.

Let's go where you'll keep on wear-in' those frills and flow-ers and

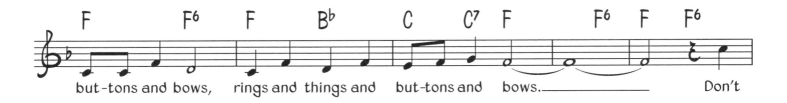

but-tons and bows, rings and things and but-tons and bows._____ Don't

bu-ry me in this prai-rie, take me where the ce-ment grows.

Let's move down to some big town__ where they love a gal by the

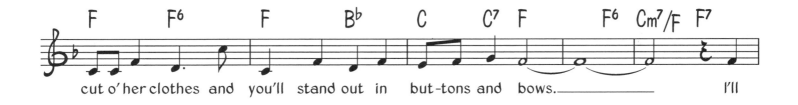

cut o' her clothes and you'll stand out in but-tons and bows._____ I'll

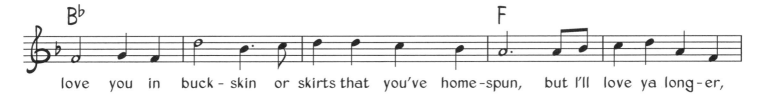

love you in buck-skin or skirts that you've home-spun, but I'll love ya long-er,

strong-er where yer friends don't tote a gun. My bones de-nounce the

buck-board bounce and the cac-tus hurts my toes. Let's va-moose where

gals keep us-in' those silks and sat-ins and lin-en that shows, and

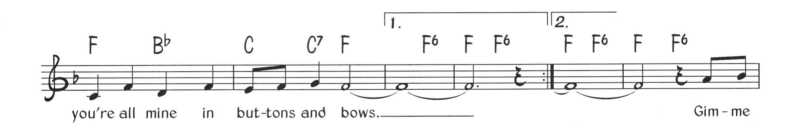

you're all mine in but-tons and bows._____ Gim-me

east-ern trim-min' where wo-men are wo-men in high silk hose and

peek-a-boo clothes and French per-fume that rocks the room and

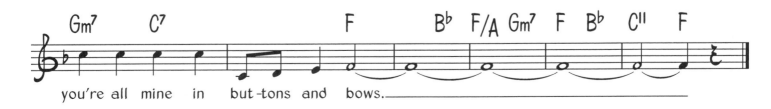

you're all mine in but-tons and bows._____

Bye Bye Baby
(Quickstep)

Words by Leo Robin ★ Music by Jule Styne

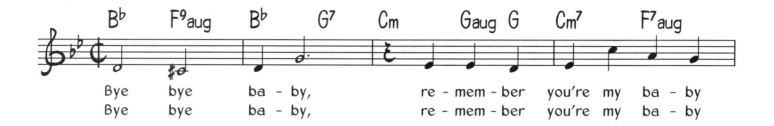

Bye bye ba - by, re - mem - ber you're my ba - by
Bye bye ba - by, re - mem - ber you're my ba - by

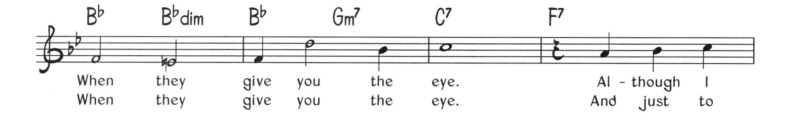

When they give you the eye. Al - though I
When they give you the eye. And just to

know that you care,— won't you write— and de - clare— That,
show that I care,— I will write— and de - clare— That

though on the loose,— you are still— on the square,—
I'm on the loose,— but I'll stay— on the square.—

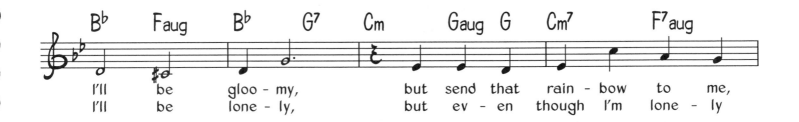

I'll be gloo - my, but send that rain - bow to me,
I'll be lone - ly, but ev - en though I'm lone - ly

Then my sha - dows will fly. Though you'll be
There'll be no oth - er guy. Though I'll be

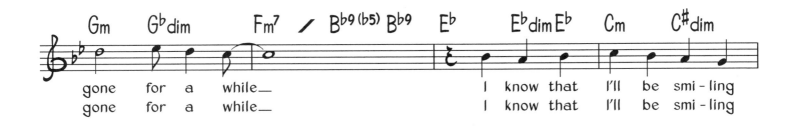

gone for a while— I know that I'll be smi - ling
gone for a while— I know that I'll be smi - ling

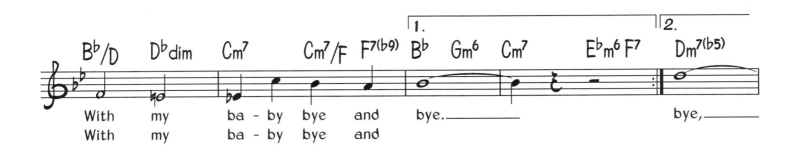

With my ba - by bye and bye.— bye,—
With my ba - by bye and

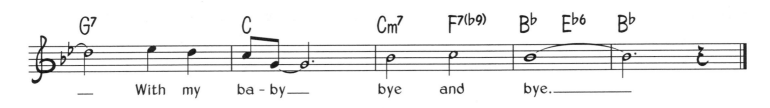

With my ba - by— bye and bye.

By The Fireside
(Old-Time Quickstep)

Words & Music by Ray Noble, Jimmy Campbell & Reg Connelly

In the gloam-ing by the fire - side, With you I'll be con -
- tent. In the gloam-ing by the fire - side, Ev -'ry hour will be well
spent. We'll see our hopes and dreams, dear, Like pic - tures in the
fire; Find - ing in its gleams, dear, Our hearts de - -
- sire. In the arm - chair by the fire - side, just big e - nough for
two, We'll be hap - py, Oh so hap - py, While we do as lov - ers
do; With no one there to no - tice A lit - tle kiss or
two, In the gloam - ing by the fire - side with you._____

Can't Help Falling In Love
(Slow Foxtrot)

Words & Music by George David Weiss, Hugo Peretti & Luigi Creatore

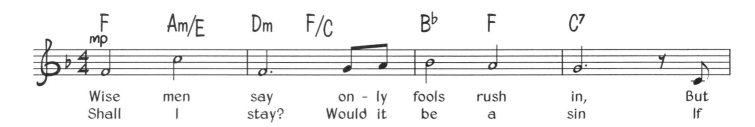

Wise men say on-ly fools rush in, But
Shall I stay? Would it be a sin If

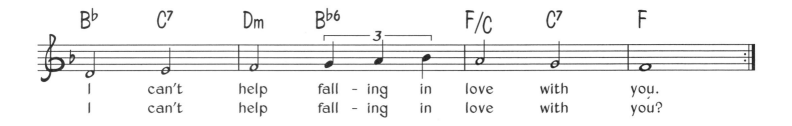

I can't help fall-ing in love with you.
I can't help fall-ing in love with you?

Like a riv-er flows sure-ly to the sea, Dar-ling, so it goes:

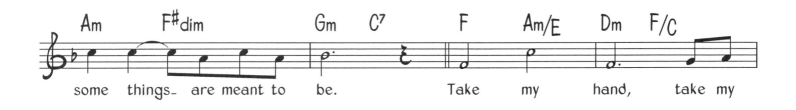

some things are meant to be. Take my hand, take my

whole life too, For I can't help fall-ing in love with

you. you. For I can't help fall-ing in love with you.

Can You Feel The Force?

(Bright Disco)

Words & Music by Chris & Eddie Amoo

Ooh, ooh, ooh, ooh, can you feel the force?

Ooh, ooh, ooh, ooh, can you feel the force?

There's a move spread-in' round the world to-day; can you feel the

force? It's with you when you work or as you

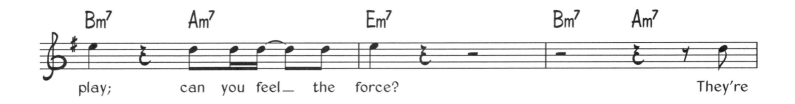

play; can you feel the force? They're

clean-ing up the streets through-out the world; can you feel the force?

Ghet - to world could have the fi - nal fall; can you feel the force?

You can feel the pres-sure lift-ing off your head; peo-ple who make

war mak-ing love in - stead. This could be the dawn-ing of an -

- oth -er time; hat-red is a stran-ger, we can see the sign.

Ooh, ooh, ooh, ooh, can you feel the force?

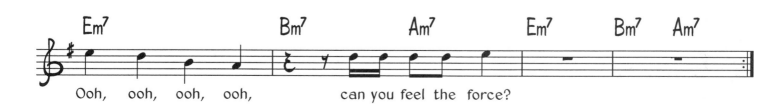

Ooh, ooh, ooh, ooh, can you feel the force?

Can't Give You Anything (But My Love)

(Disco Smooch)

Words & Music by George David Weiss, Hugo Peretti & Luigi Creatore

1. If I had

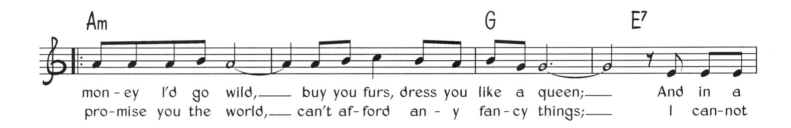

mon - ey I'd go wild,___ buy you furs, dress you like a queen;___ And in a
pro - mise you the world,___ can't af-ford an - y fan-cy things;___ I can-not

chauf-fered lim - ou - sine___ we'd look so fine.___ But I'm an
buy you dia-mond rings,___ no string of pearls.___ But my de -

or - di - na - ry guy___ and my pock - ets are emp - ty;___ Just an
- vo-tion I will give___ all my life just to you girl,___ My de -

or - di - na - ry guy___ but I'm yours till I die.___
- vo-tion I will give___ for as long as I live.___

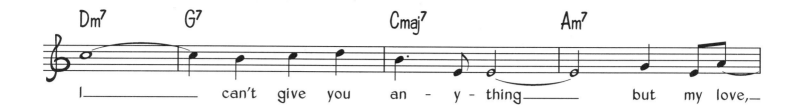

Dm⁷   G⁷   Cmaj⁷   Am⁷

I_____ can't give you an - y - thing_____ but my love,___

Dm   Dm⁷/G   C⁶

_____ but my love._____

Dm⁷   G⁷   Cmaj⁷   Am⁷

I_____ can't give you an - y - thing_____ but my love,___

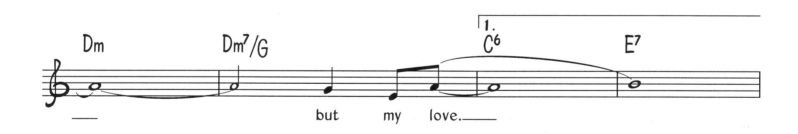

Dm   Dm⁷/G   1. C⁶   E⁷

___ but my love.____

Am   N.C.   2. C⁶

2. I can-not _____

Champagne Charlie
(Old-Time)

Words by H.J. Whymark ★ Music by Alfred Lee

Cham - pagne Char - lie is my name,

Cham - pagne drink - ing is my game,

There's no drink as good as Fizz! Fizz! Fizz!

I'll drink ev - 'ry drop there is, is, is!

All round town it is the same, By

Pop! Pop! Pop! I rose to fame;

I'm the i - dol of the bar - maids, And

Cham - pagne Char - lie is my name.

Chantilly Lace
(Rock 'N' Roll)

Words & Music by J.P. Richardson

Chan - til - ly Lace___ and a pret-ty face___ And a po-ny tail___

___ hang-in' down,___ Wig - gle in her walk and a gig - gle in her

talk,   Makes the world go 'round,_____ Ain't

noth - in' in this world like a big-eyed girl___ To make me

act so fun - ny, make me spend my mon - ey, Make me

feel real loose like a long - necked goose, like a girl._____

Choo Choo Samba
(Samba)

Words by Jack Fishman ★ Music by B.P. Godinho

A chick-ar-ack-a choo, chick-ar-ack-a choo, A chick-ar-ack-a
go thro' sun-ny Me-xi-co, And then to Pa-na-

choo choo is the train for you, A-cross the Ri-o Grande to sun-ny Sam-ba
-ma from Ni-ca-ra-gu-a. And all a-long the way the na-tives shout "O-

land To where the sam-ba bands will play your eve-nings through. On that Ma-ra-ca
-le!" They wish that you could stay, but know you're go-ing far. From Ven-ez-ue-la

ride, you shake from side to side; That rail-way's got a rhy-thm you en-joy to
you will chick-ar-ack-a choo. And when you hear the sam-ba you know where you

do. And when you trav-el on that train, you wan-na choo choo back a-gain; Ev-'ry-
are. You choo choo on to U-ra-guay, and down to Ar-gen-ti-na way, To the

Cocktails For Two
(Foxtrot)

Words & Music by Arthur Johnston & Sam Coslow

In some se-clu-ded ren-dez - vous,_____ that ov-er-looks the a-ve-

- nue,_____ With some-one shar-ing a de-light-ful chat of

this and that and cock-tails for two.__ As we en-joy a ci-ga-

- rette_____ to some ex-qui-site chan-son-ette,_____ Two hands are sure to sly-ly

meet be-neath a ser-vi-ette with cock-tails for two.__ My head may go

reel - ing, but my heart will be o - be - di-ent, With in-tox-i-ca-ting

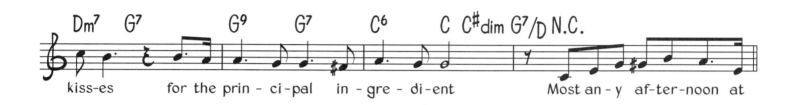

kiss-es for the prin - ci-pal in - gre - di-ent Most an - y af-ter-noon at

five_____ we'll be so glad we're both a - live._____Then may-be for-tune will com-

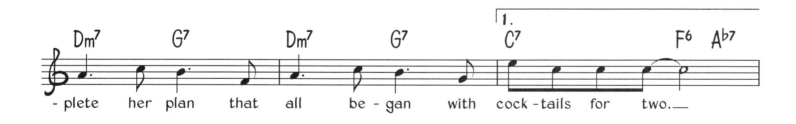

- plete her plan that all be - gan with cock - tails for two._

In some se - clu -ded ren - dez- cock - tails for two._____

Come Back To Erin

(Irish - Slow Foxtrot)

Traditional

1. Come back to E - rin, Ma - vour - neen, Ma - vour - neen,
(Verses 2, 3 see block lyric)

Come back, A-roon, to the land of thy birth.____ Come with the sham - rocks and

spring - time, Ma - vour - neen, And its Kil - lar - ney shall ring with our mirth.

Sure, when we lent ye to beau - ti - ful Eng - land, Lit - tle we thought of the

lone win - ter days. Lit - tle we thought of the hush of the star - shine

Ov - er the moun - tains, the buffs and the bays. Then come back to E - rin, Ma-

- vour-neen, Ma - vour - neen, Come back a - gain to the land of thy birth.____

Come back to E - rin, Ma -vour-neen, Ma - vour -neen, And__ its Kil - lar - ney shall

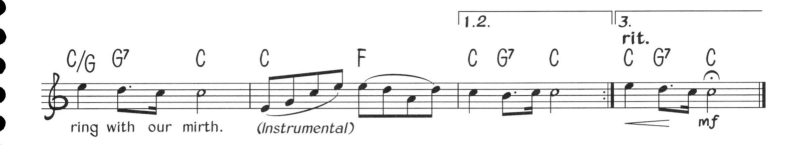

ring with our mirth.　(Instrumental)

Verse 2
Over the green sea, Mavourneen, Mavourneen,
Long shone the white sail that bore thee away,
Riding the white waves that fair summer morning,
Just like a Mayflow'r afloat on the bay.
Oh, but my heart sank when clouds came between us,
Like a grey curtain, the rain falling down;
Hid from my sad eyes the path o'er the ocean;
Far, far away where my colleen had flown.

Verse 3
Oh, may the angels awaking and sleeping
Watch o'er my bird in the land far away.
And it's my prayers I'll consign to their keeping:
Care for my jewel by night and by day.
When by the fireside I watch the bright embers,
Then all my heart flies to England and thee,
Craving to know if my darling remembers,
Or if her thoughts may be crossing to me.

Chick Chick Chicken
(Novelty Quickstep)

Words & Music by Fred Holt, Thomas McGhee & Irving King

Chick, chick, chick, chick, chick-en,___ Lay a lit-tle egg for

me, Chick, chick, chick, chick, chick-en,___ I

want one for my tea. Oh, I have-n't had an egg since

Eas-ter, And now it's half past three, So, chick, chick, chick, chick,

chick-en,___ Lay a lit-tle egg for me.

Come Dancing
(Quickstep)

Words & Music by Hubert David & Ray Downes

(Instrumental)   Come

danc -ing,   it's   the   thing,—   It's   the   thing—   for   you.—

—   Come   danc -ing,   it   can   bring—   Joy   and   ju - bi -

- la - tion,   And   what   a   ton - ic   for   the   na - tion!   Get   weav -ing

on   your   toes;—   Danc -ing   is   a   hap - py   re - ci - pe.

—   Join   in   the   laugh -ter,   And   if   it's   fun   and

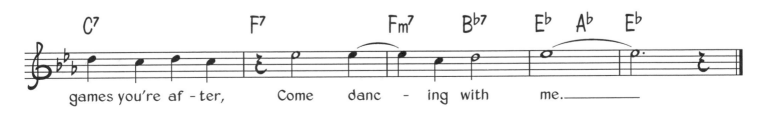

games   you're   af -ter,   Come   danc - ing   with   me.—

Come Live Your Life With Me

(Slow Waltz)

Words by Billy Meshel & Larry Kusik ★ Music by Nino Rota

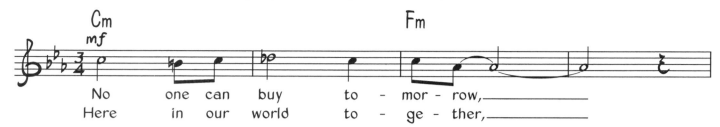

No one can buy to - mor - row,_____
Here in our world to - ge - ther,_____

No one can sell their sor - row;_____
Love will go on for - ev - er;_____

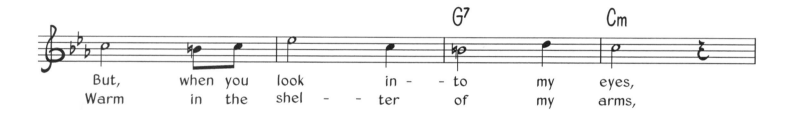

But, when you look in - to my eyes,
Warm in the shel - - ter of my arms,

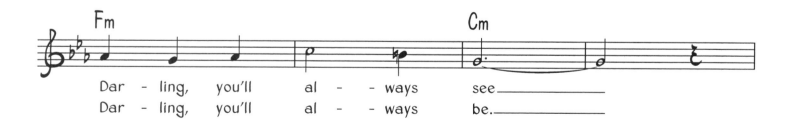

Dar - ling, you'll al - - ways see_____
Dar - ling, you'll al - - ways be._____

Love._____ I will give you love;_____
Love,_____ I will give you love;_____

Come live your life with me.

We'll have our good times and, ev - en in sad times, with

love, we will find a way.

No - thing else mat - ters but lov - ing each oth - er the

way that we do to - day.

Cruising Down The River
(Old-Time Waltz)

Words & Music by Eily Beadell & Nell Tollerton

Cruis - ing down the riv - er _____ on a

Sun - - day aft - - er - noon, _____ With

one you love, the sun a - bove,

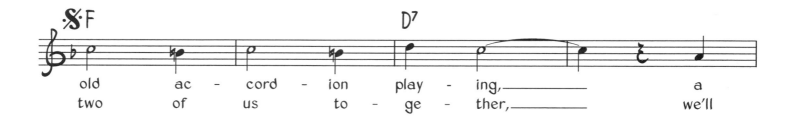

wait - ing for the moon. _____ The

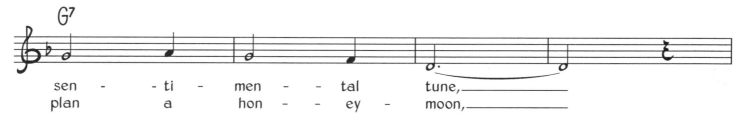

old ac - cord - ion play - ing, _____ a
two of us to - ge - ther, _____ we'll

sen - - ti - men - tal tune,
plan a hon - ey - moon,

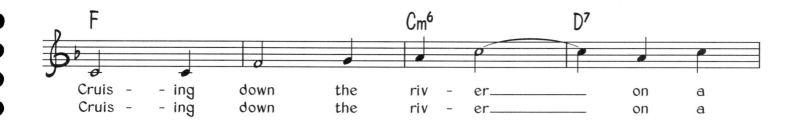

Cruis – – ing down the riv – er_____ on a
Cruis – – ing down the riv – er_____ on a

Fine

Sun – – day af – – ter – noon._____ The
Sun – – day af – – ter – noon._____

birds a – bove all sing of love, a

gen – – tle sweet re – – frain._____ The

winds a – round all make a sound like

D. %̸ al Fine

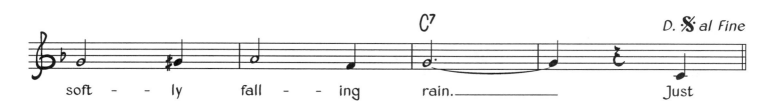

soft – – ly fall – – ing rain._____ Just

D.I.S.C.O.
(Medium Disco)

Words & Music by Daniel Vangarde & Jean Kluger

D. I. S. C. O.,___ she is D. I. S. C. O.___ She is

D. I. S. C. O.,___ she is D. I. S. C. O.___

She is

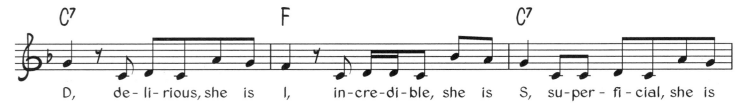

D, de-li-rious, she is I, in-cre-di-ble, she is S, su-per-fi-cial, she is

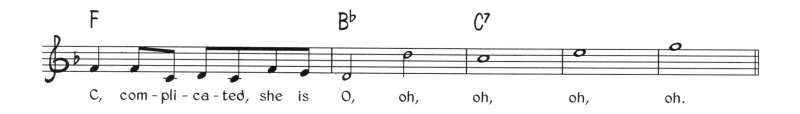

C, com-pli-ca-ted, she is O, oh, oh, oh, oh.

D. I. S. C. O.____ she is D. I. S. C. O.,____ she is

D. I. S. C. O.,____ she is D. I. S. C. O.____

She is D. I. S. C. O.,__

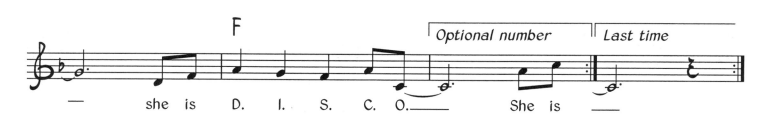

Optional number ‖ *Last time*

__ she is D. I. S. C. O.____ She is __

Dancing Queen
(Medium Disco)

Words & Music by Benny Andersson, Björn Ulvaeus & Stig Anderson

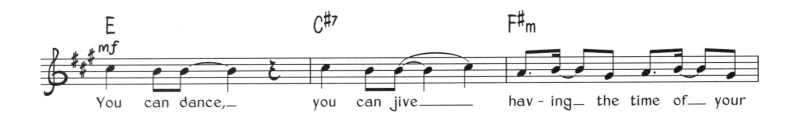

You can dance,— you can jive— hav - ing— the time of— your

life.— Oh see that girl,— watch that— scene— dig - gin' the

danc - ing— queen,———

Fri - day nights— and the lights are low,— look - ing out— for a place to go,—

Oh_____ where they play__ the right mu - sic

get - ting in__ the swing,__ you come to look for a king.__

An - y - bo - dy could be that guy,__ Night is young__ and the mu - sic's
You're a teas - er, you turn 'em on,__ Leave 'em burn - ing and then you're

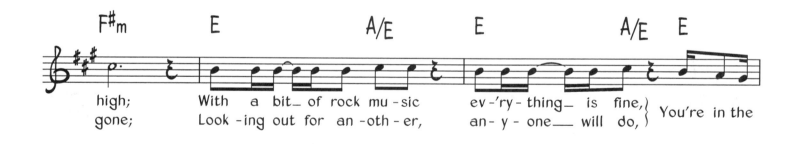

high; With a bit__ of rock mu - sic ev -'ry - thing__ is fine,⎫ You're in the
gone; Look -ing out for an -oth - er, an - y - one__ will do,⎭

mood for a dance.__ And when__ you get the__ chance_____

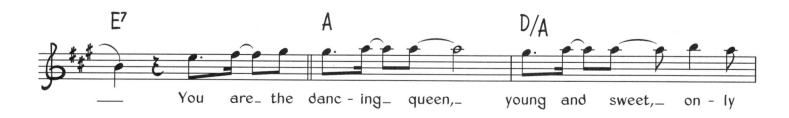

___ You are__ the danc - ing__ queen,__ young and sweet,__ on - ly

sev - en - teen._____ Danc-ing_ queen,_ feel the_ beat_ from the

tam - bou - rine._____ You can dance,_ you can jive,_____

hav - ing_ the time of_ your life.___ Oh_____ see that girl,_

watch that_ scene_ dig-gin' the danc - ing_ queen._____

Repeat and fade

Dig-gin' the danc - ing_ queen._____

Dear Old Donegal
(Irish Jig)

Words & Music by Steve Graham

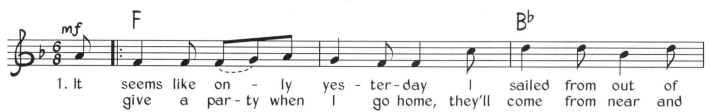

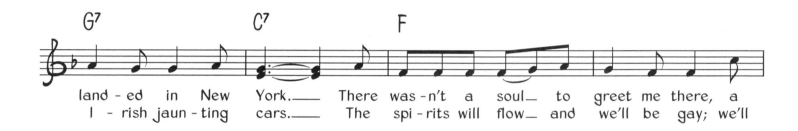

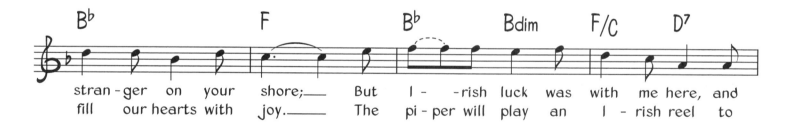

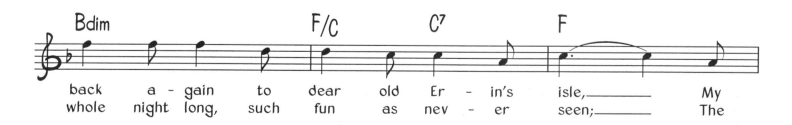

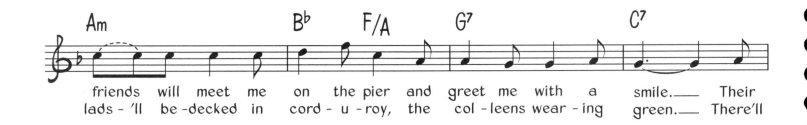

friends will meet me on the pier and greet me with a smile.___ Their
lads-'ll be-decked in cord-u-roy, the col-leens wear-ing green.___ There'll

fa - - ces, sure, I've al - - most for - got, I've
be thou - sands there that I nev - er saw, I've

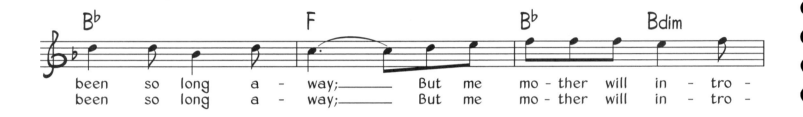

been so long a - way;___ But me mo - ther will in - tro -
been so long a - way;___ But me mo - ther will in - tro -

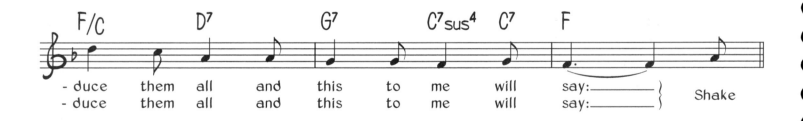

- duce them all and this to me will say:___ } Shake
- duce them all and this to me will say:___

hands with your Un - -cle Mike, me boy, And here is your sis - ter

Kate;___ and there's the girl you used to swing down

74

by the gar - den gate._____ Shake hands with all of the

neigh - bours,_ and kiss the col - leens all._____ You're as wel - come as the

flow'rs in May to dear old Don - e - gal._____ 2. They'll - gal.

Bran - ni - gan, Fan - ni - gan, Mil - li - gan, Gil - li - gan, Duf - fy, Mc - Cuf - fy, Ma -
Ma - di - gan, Ca - di - gan, La - ni - han, Fla - ni - han, Fa - gan, O' - Ha - gan, O' -

- la - chy, Ma - hone, Raf - fer - ty, Laf - fer - ty, Don - nel - ly, Con - nel - ly,
- Hoo - li - han, Flynn, Sha - ni - han, Ma - ni - han, Fo - gar - ty, Ho - gar - ty,

Doo - ley, O' - Hoo - ley, Mul - down - ey, Ma - lone. - Guin - ness, Mc - Guinn. Shake
Kel - ly, O' - Kel - ly, Mc -

Dinner At Eight

(Quickstep)

Words by Dorothy Fields ★ Music by Jimmy McHugh

In your ap-point-ment book you'll see, You and I have a date.

Let me re-fresh your me-mo-ry: Dar-ling, you can't be late

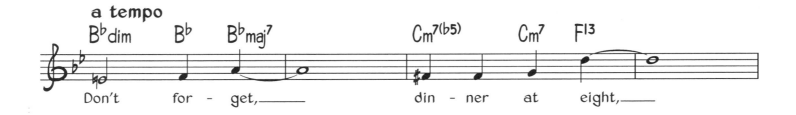

Don't for - get,___ din - ner at eight,___

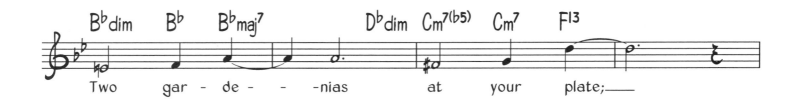

Two gar - de - - nias at your plate;___

Un - der the ta - ble our hands will meet,___

We should be a - ble to be dis - creet.___

Lights are dim,___ moon - light a - bove;___

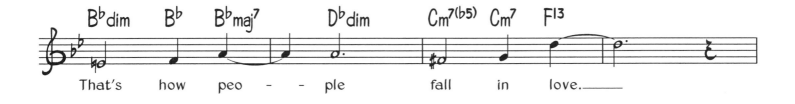

That's how peo - - ple fall in love.___

Just tell your mo - ther you might be late!___

Don't for - - get, din - ner at eight.___

Disco Inferno
(Bright Disco)

Words & Music by Leroy Green & Ron Kersey

Burn__ ba-by, burn. Burn__ ba-by, burn.

Two mass fires,__ yes!__ One hun-dred stor-eys__ high.__

__ Peo-ple__ get-tin' loose__ y'all, you're get-ting

down on__ the roof.__ The folks were flam-

-in' out of con-trol,__ it was so__

__ en-ter-tain-ing when the boo-gie start-ed to ex-

- plode, I heard some - bo - dy say: Burn___ ba - by, burn. (Disco inferno) Burn_

___ ba - by, burn. (Burn that mother down) Up a - bove my

head, I hear mu - sic in the air._____

That makes me know there's a par - ty some - where.___

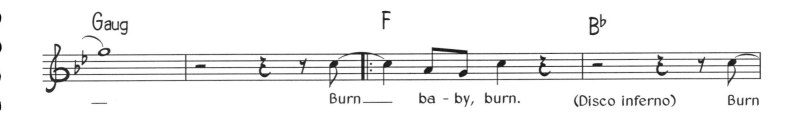
___ Burn___ ba - by, burn. (Disco inferno) Burn

Optional number | Last time

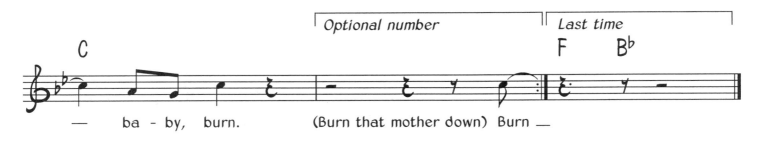
___ ba - by, burn. (Burn that mother down) Burn ___

Dinah
(Quickstep)

Words by Sam Lewis & Joe Young ★ Music by Harry Akst

Dizzy Miss Lizzie
(Rock 'N' Roll)

Words & Music by Larry Williams

1. You make me diz-zy, Miss Liz-zie, the way you rock and roll!
(Verse 2 see block lyric)

You make me diz-zy, Miss Liz-zie, when we do the stroll!

Come on, Miss Liz-zie, love me 'fore I get too old!

Come on and kiss me, ba-by, put your lit-tle hand in mine.

You make me diz-zy, Miss Liz-zie; girl, you look so fine.

You're just a-rock-in' and a-roll-in', I sure do wish you were mine!

2. You make me diz-zy, Miss

Verse 2
You make me dizzy, Miss Lizzie, when you call my name.
Oh, oh, oh, oh, oh baby, say, you're driving me insane!
Come on, come on, come on baby.
I want to be your lover man.
Run and tell your mama, I want you to be my bride.
Run and tell your brother, baby, don't run and hide.
You make me dizzy Miss Lizzie,
And I want to marry you.

Don't Dilly Dally On The Way

(Old-Time)

Words & Music by Fred W. Leigh & Charles Collins

I walked be-hind with my old cock lin-net, But I dil-lied and
dal-lied, dal-lied and dil-lied, Lost the van and don't know where to
roam_____ You can't trust a 'spe-cial' like an old-time
cop-per When you can't find your way home._____

Verse 2
I gave a helping hand with the marble wash-hand stand,
And straight we wasn't getting on so bad.
All at once the car-man bloke had an accident and broke
Well the nicest bit of china that we had.
You'll understand of course I was cross about the loss,
Same as any other human woman would,
But I soon got over that, what with 'two-out' and a chat,
'Cos it's little things like that what does you good!
My old man etc.

Verse 3
Oh, I'm in such a mess, I don't know the new address,
Don't even know the blessed neighbourhood;
And I feel as if I might have to stay out all the night,
And that ain't a-goin' to do me any good.
I don't make no complaint, but I'm coming over faint,
What I want now is a good substantial feed;
And I sort o' kind o' feel if I don't soon have a meal,
I shall have to rob the linnet of his seed!
My old man etc.

Don't Laugh At Me ('Cause I'm A Fool)
(Foxtrot)

Words & Music by Norman Wisdom & June Tremayne

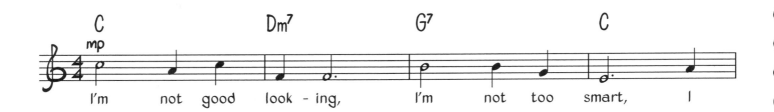

I'm not good look-ing, I'm not too smart, I

may be fool-ish but I've got a heart.

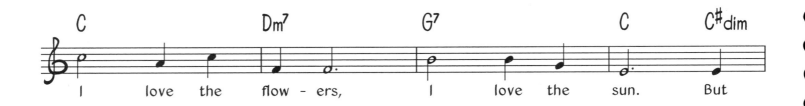

I love the flow-ers, I love the sun. But

when I try to love the girls they laugh at me and run.____

Don't laugh at me 'cause I'm a fool,____

I know it's true. Yes! I'm a fool.____

Dm⁷ ... G¹³ ... G⁷ ... C ... Em ... Am

No one seems to care, I'd give the world to share my life with

Am⁷ ... D¹³ ... D⁷ ... Dm⁷ ... G⁷

some - one_____ who real - ly loves me.

C ... Em ... Am⁷ ... Dm⁷ ... G⁷

I see them all fall - ing in love,_____ But

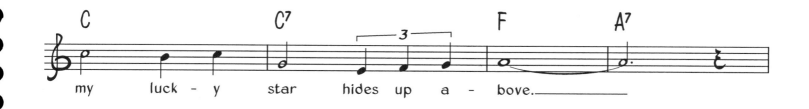

C ... C⁷ ... F ... A⁷

my luck - y star hides up a - bove._____

F ... F♯dim ... C⁶ ... Em⁷⁽ᵇ⁵⁾ A⁹

Some day may - be my star will shine on me,

Dm⁷ ... G⁷ ... C Fm C

Don't laugh at me 'cause I'm a fool._____

Don't Stop The Music

(Medium Disco)

Words & Music by Jonah Ellis, Lonnie Simmons & Alisa Yarbrough

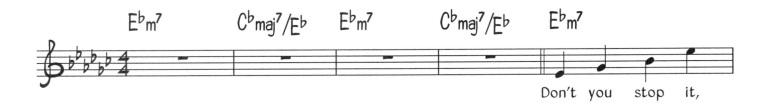

Don't you stop it,

don't you stop, stop the mu - sic. Don't you

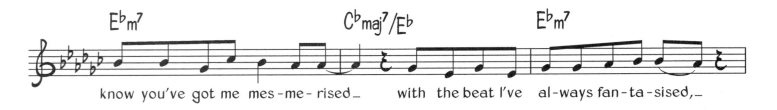

know you've got me mes-me-rised with the beat I've al-ways fan-ta-sised,

don't stop the mu-sic 'cause it tends to soothe. I can tell you

want to groove. Don't you stop it don't you stop, stop the mu-

- sic. Beat keeps go-ing 'round and 'round, turns me up-side

down. I just want to rock you, oh,

88

Dream Baby (How Long Must I Dream?)
(Foxtrot)

Words & Music by Cindy Walker

Dream ba-by got____ me dream-in' sweet dreams. The whole day

through. Dream ba-by got____ me dream-in' sweet dreams,

Night time too; I love you and____ I'm dream-in' of you,

But that won't do.____ Dream ba-by make

____ me stop my dream-in', You can make my dreams____ come true.____

Sweet dreams____ ba-by,

Sweet dreams____ ba-by,

Sweet dreams____ ba-by,

How long must I dream?____

Dreamboat
(Foxtrot)

Words & Music by Jack Hoffman

Everybody Loves A Lover
(Quickstep)

Words & Music by Robert Allen & Richard Adler

Ev - 'ry - bo - dy loves a lov - er, I'm a lov - er, ev - 'ry - bo - dy loves me. An - y - how, that's how I feel. Wow! I feel just like a Pol - ly - an - na. I should wor - ry, not for noth - in', Ev - 'ry - bo - dy loves me, yes they do. And I love ev - 'ry - bo - dy_____ Since I fell in love with you._____

Everything Stops For Tea
(Quickstep)

Words & Music by Maurice Sigler, Al Goodhart & Al Hoffman

1. Oh, the fact-'ries may be roar-ing, With a boom-a-lack-a, zoom-a-lack-a whee! But there is-n't an-y roar when the
   may be play-ing foot-ball, And the crowd is yell-ing: "Kill the ref-er-ee," But no mat-ter what the score; when the

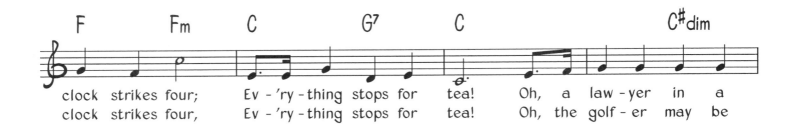

clock strikes four; Ev-'ry-thing stops for tea! Oh, a law-yer in a
clock strikes four, Ev-'ry-thing stops for tea! Oh, the golf-er may be

court-room, In the mid-dle of an a-li-mo-ny plea, Has to
golf-ing, And is just a-bout to make a hole in three, But it

stop and help 'em pour when the clock strikes four; Ev-'ry-thing stops for
al-ways gets him sore when the clock strikes four; Ev-'ry-thing stops for

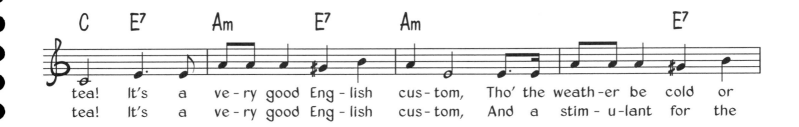

tea! It's a ve-ry good Eng-lish cus-tom, Tho' the weath-er be cold or
tea! It's a ve-ry good Eng-lish cus-tom, And a stim-u-lant for the

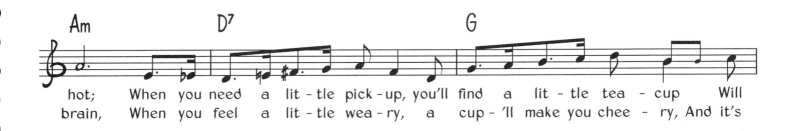

hot; When you need a lit-tle pick-up, you'll find a lit-tle tea-cup Will
brain, When you feel a lit-tle wea-ry, a cup-'ll make you chee-ry, And it's

al-ways hit the spot. Oh, the sol-diers may be fight-ing, In the
cheap-er than cham-pagne. Now I know just why Franz Schu-bert Did-n't

trench-es or a bat-tle-ship at sea, But there is-n't an-y war when the
fin-ish his un-fin-ish'd Sym-pho-ny; He might have writ-ten more, but the

clock strikes four; Ev-'ry-thing stops for tea! 2. Oh, they tea!
clock struck four! Ev-'ry-thing stops for

Fanlight Fanny
(Quickstep)

Words & Music by George Formby, Frederick Cliffe, Harry Gifford & Clinton Ford

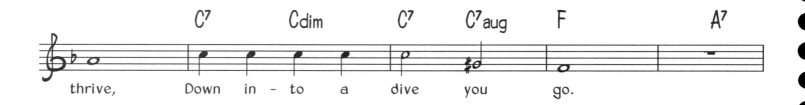

Up the West End, That's the best end, Where the night clubs

thrive, Down in-to a dive you go.

There's a jazz queen, She's a has been, Has been Lord knows what.

Ev-'ry night she's there on show. She

dan-ces un-der-neath a mag-ic spell,_____ She's

full of charm and gin and scotch as well!_____ She's

six-ty-six but looks six-teen, Her friends don't know her now her

face is clean,— Fan-light Fan-ny the frow-sy night club queen.

See her glide a-round the floor, Then glide a-round in-to the pub next door,

Fan-light Fan-ny the frow-sy night club queen. She looks

swell in the lime',— A queen all the time,— You get your mo-ney's worth,

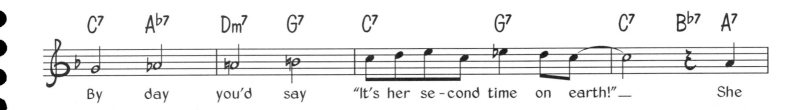

By day you'd say "It's her se-cond time on earth!"— She

waltz-es in the West End shops, Then waltz-es out a-gain be-tween two cops,—

Fan-light Fan-ny the frow-sy night club queen.———

Farrago
(Cha-Cha)

By Barry White

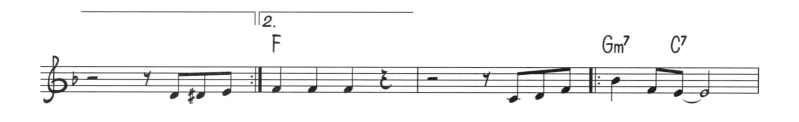

Feed The Birds
(Waltz)

Words & Music by Richard M. Sherman & Robert B. Sherman

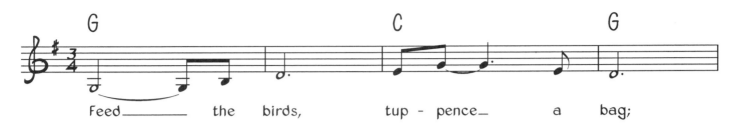

Feed the birds, tup - pence a bag;

tup - pence, tup - pence, tup - pence a bag.

"Feed the birds." That's what she cries,

While ov - er - head her birds fill the skies. All a -

- round the ca - the - dral, the saints and a - post - les Look

down as she sells her wares. Al -

- though you can't see it, you know they are smi - ling Each

time some - one shows that he cares._____

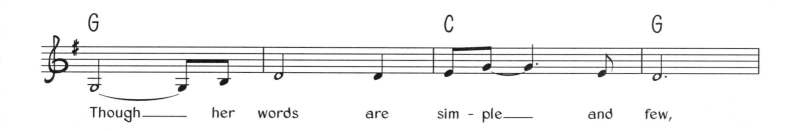
Though_____ her words are sim - ple_____ and few,

Lis - ten,____ lis - ten,____ she's call - ing____ to you.

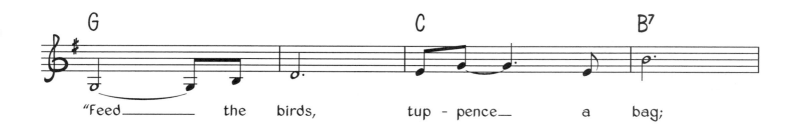
"Feed_____ the birds, tup - pence____ a bag;

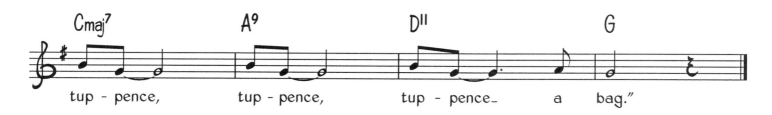
tup - pence, tup - pence, tup - pence_ a bag."

Fascination

(Waltz)

Music by F.D. Marchetti ★ English Words by Dick Manning

It was fas-ci-na-tion I know,_____ And it might have

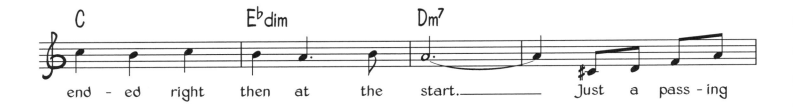

end-ed right then at the start._____ Just a pass-ing

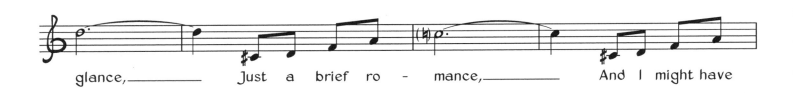

glance,_____ Just a brief ro-mance,_____ And I might have

gone on my way emp-ty heart-ed._____ It was fas-ci-

-na-tion, I know,_____ See-ing you a-

C   E♭dim   Dm

- lone   with   the   moon - light   a - bove._____   Then   I   touched your

Dm⁷   G¹³   G⁷

hand   and   next   mo - ment   I   kissed   you;_____   fas - ci - na - tion

Dm⁷   G⁷⁽♭⁹⁾   C   F

turned   to   love._____   Then   it   seemed   that   the

stars   in   the   night   had   stopped   in   their   flight,   so

C⁷

bright   was   their   gleam._____   Time   stood   still   as   we

danced   in   a   whirl,   a   boy   and   a   girl   a -

B⁷   C⁷   F   C⁷   F

- lone   in   a   dream._____   What   a   won - der - ful

feel - ing of bliss, a - wait - ing each kiss that thrilled me a -

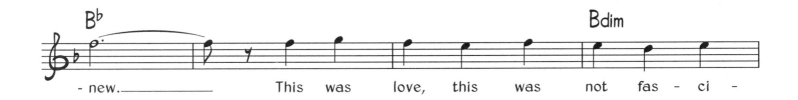

- new._____ This was love, this was not fas - ci -

- na - tion, I knew as I thrilled to the won - der of

you._____ It was fas - ci - na - - tion, I know,____

__ See - ing you a - lone with the moon - light a - bove.____

__ Then I touched your hand, and next mo - ment I kissed you;____

__ fas - ci - na - tion turned to love._____

Giddy Up A Ding Dong
(Rock 'N' Roll)

Words & Music by Freddie Bell & Peppino Lattanzi

Verse 2:
We rode and we rode the whole night through,
The horse was tired and I was too;
But I had a date with my gal at eight.
Come on Ding Dong, we can't be late.
I said giddy-up, (etc.)

Verse 3:
When I got to my girl's house the lights were down,
She was sitting on the porch with the toughest guy in town.
If I butted in he might decide to use force;
I thought to myself: stick with the horse!
I said giddy-up, (etc.)

Galway Bay
(Irish - Foxtrot)

Words & Music by Arthur Colahan

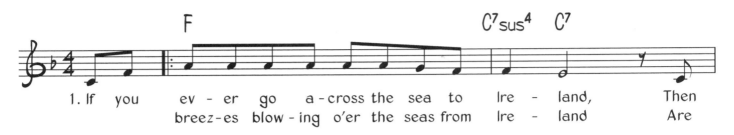

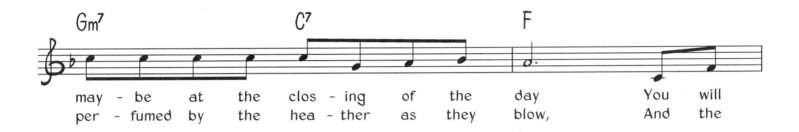

1. If you ev - er go a - cross the sea to Ire - land, Then
breez - es blow - ing o'er the seas from Ire - land Are

may - be at the clos - ing of the day You will
per - fumed by the hea - ther as they blow, And the

sit and watch the moon rise ov - er Clad - dagh And____
wo - men in the up - lands dig - ging pra - ties Speak a

see the sun go down on Gal - way Bay. Just to
lan - guage that the stran - gers do not know. For the

hear a - gain the rip - ple of the trout stream, The
stran - gers came and tried to teach us their way, They

wo - men in the mea-dows mak-ing   hay,   And to   sit be-side a turf fire in the
scorned us just for be - ing what we   are.   But they might as well go chas-ing af -ter

cab - in   And   watch the bare-foot Gos - soons at their   play!   2. For the
moon -beams, Or   light   a   pen - ny can - dle from a

star.   3. And if   there is going to be a life here - af - ter,   And

some-how I am sure there's going to   be,   I will ask the Lord to let me make my

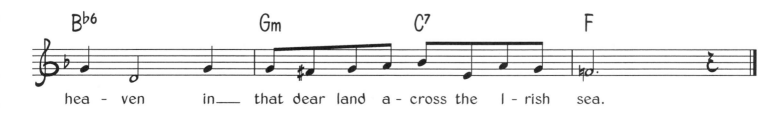

hea - ven   in___ that dear land a - cross the I - rish   sea.

Get Down On It
(Medium Disco)

Words & Music by Ronald Bell, Eumir Deodato, Robert Mickens, James Taylor, Charles Smith, Robert Bell & George Brown

Girl Talk
(Slow Foxtrot)

Words by Bobby Troup ★ Music by Neal Hefti

They like to chat a-bout the dress - es they will wear to-night;

They chew the fat a-bout their tress - es and the neigh - bour's fight:

In - con - se - quen - tial things that men don't real - ly care to know

Be - come es - sen - tial things that wo - men find so "ap - pro - po".

But that's a dame, they're all the same; it's just a game. They call it girl talk,

girl talk. They all me-ow a-bout the ups and downs of all their friends.

The "who", the "how", the "why"; they dish the dirt, it nev-er ends.

The weak-er sex, the speak-er sex we mor-tal males be-hold,

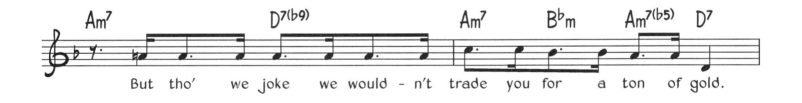

But tho' we joke we would-n't trade you for a ton of gold.

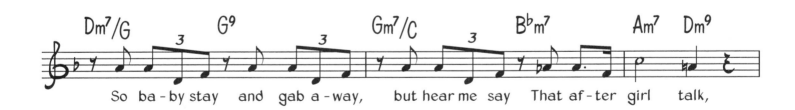

So ba-by stay and gab a-way, but hear me say That af-ter girl talk,

talk to me.   me.

The Girl I Left Behind Me
(Scottish/American Reel)

Traditional

I____ struck the trail in sev - en - ty - nine, The

herd strung out____ be - - hind me, As I

jogged a - - long my mind ran back to the

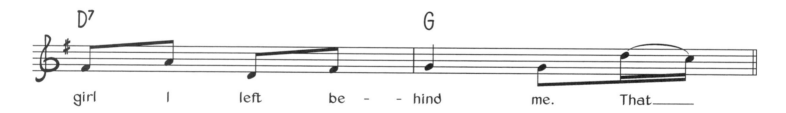

girl I left be - - hind me. That____

sweet lit - tle girl, That true lit - tle girl. The

girl I left be - hind me, That____ sweet lit - tle girl, That

true lit - tle girl. The girl I left be - - hind me.

The Glory Of Love

(Foxtrot)

Words & Music by Billy Hill

Good Golly Miss Molly
(Rock 'N' Roll)

Words & Music by Robert Blackwell & John Marascalco

Good gol - ly Miss Mol - ly, yeah you sure_ like a ball!_

_ Well Good gol - ly Miss Mol - ly,

yeah you sure_ like a ball!_____ When you're shak - in' and a

shout - in', can't you hear_ your mom - ma call?

Well, from the ear - ly, ear - ly morn - in' to the ear - ly, ear - ly night, When I

caught Miss Mol - ly rock - in' at the House Of Blue Lights,_ Ooh! Good

gol - ly Miss Mol - ly,   yeah you sure_ like a ball!_

When you're rock - in' and a - roll - in',   can't you hear_ your mom - ma

call?   Well now, Mom - ma, Pop - pa told me "Son, you'd

bet - ter watch your step!" What I knew a - bout Miss Mol - ly, got - ta

watch my dad - dy my - self! Good gol - - ly Miss Mol - ly,

yeah you sure_ like a ball!_   When you're shak - in' and a

shout - in',   can't you hear_ your mom - ma call?_

Good Times

(Medium Disco)

Words & Music by Bernard Edwards & Nile Rodgers

Good times, these are the good times;

leave your cares be - hind, these are the good times.

Good times, these are the good times,

Our new state of mind; these are the good times.

Hap-py days are here a-gain, the time is right for

mak-ing friends, let's get to-geth - er how 'bout a

quar-ter to ten?_ come to-mor-row, let's all do it a-gain._

Boys will be boys, bet-ter let them have their toys;

girls will be girls, cute po-ny-tails and curls. Must put an end to this

stress and strife. I think I want to live the sport-ing life. Good

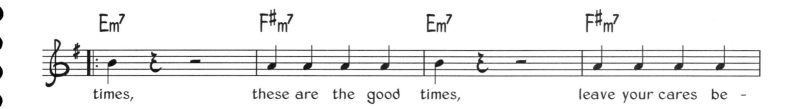
times, these are the good times, leave your cares be -

Optional number | Last time

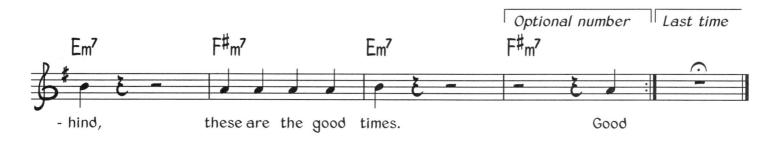
- hind, these are the good times. Good

He'll Have To Go
(Waltz)

Words & Music by Joe Allison & Audrey Allison

Put your sweet lips a lit-tle clo-ser to the phone,_____ Let's pre-

-tend that we're to-ge-ther all a-lone._____ I'll tell the

man to turn the juke-box way down low,_____ And you can

tell your friend there with you he'll have to go._____ Whis-per

to me,_____ tell me do you love me true,_____ Or is

he hold-ing you the way I do?_____ Tho' love is

blind, make up your mind, I've got to know;_____ Should I

hang up,— or will you tell him— he'll have to go.——— You can't

say the words I want to hear while you're with an-oth-er man. If you

want me, an-swer yes or no; dar-ling, I will un-der-stand. Put your

sweet lips— a lit-tle clo-ser— to the phone,——— ·Let's pre -

- tend that we're to-ge-ther all a - lone——— I'll tell the man to turn the

juke - box way down low,——— And you can tell your friend there

with you— he'll have to go.——— Put your go.———

Hey, Look Me Over
(Quickstep)

Words by Carolyn Leigh ★ Music by Cy Coleman

Hey, look me ov - er, lend me an ear;

Fresh out of clo - ver mort - gaged up to here! But

don't pass the plate, folks; don't pass the cup. I

fig - ure when - ev - er you're down and out the on - ly way is up! And I'll be

up like a rose - bud high on the vine. Don't thumb your nose, bud,

take a tip from mine. I'm a lit - tle bit short of the el - bow room, but

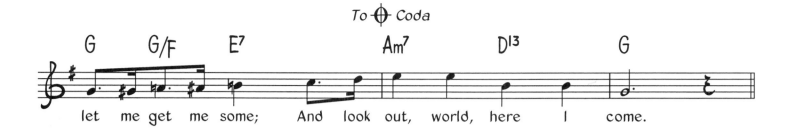

let me get me some; And look out, world, here I come.

No - bo - dy in the world was ev - er with - out a pray'r.

How can you win the world if no - bo - dy knows you're there?

Kid, when you need the crowd, the tick - ets are hard to sell;

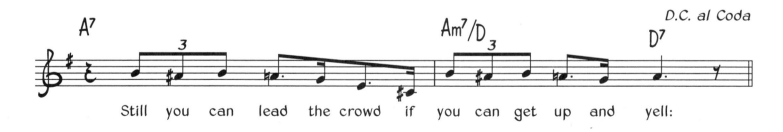

Still you can lead the crowd if you can get up and yell:

out, world, here I come! (Instrumental)

119

Hava Nagila

(Jewish)

Traditional

Hi-Heel Sneakers

(Rock 'N' Roll)

Words & Music by Robert Higgenbotham

The Hot Canary
(Novelty Quickstep)

Words by Ray Gilbert ★ Music by Paul Nero

I Don't Know Why (I Just Do)

(Foxtrot)

Words by Roy Turk ★ Music by Fred Ahlert

I don't know why__ I love you like I do;__

I don't know why,__ I just do. I don't know why__ you

thrill me like you do;__ I don't know why,__ you just do. You

nev - er seem to want my ro - manc - ing, The on - ly time you hold me is

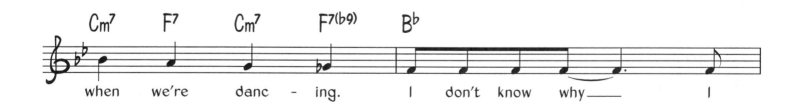

when we're danc - ing. I don't know why__ I

love you like I do;__ I don't know why,__ I just do.

I Came, I Saw, I Conga'd

(Conga)

Words & Music by James Cavanaugh, John Redmond & Frank Weldon

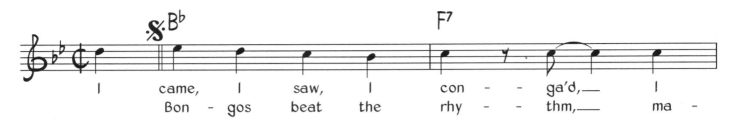

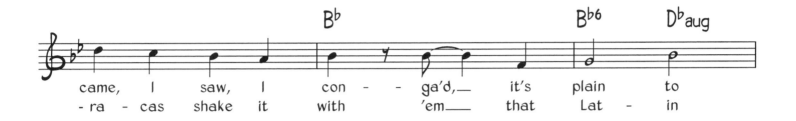

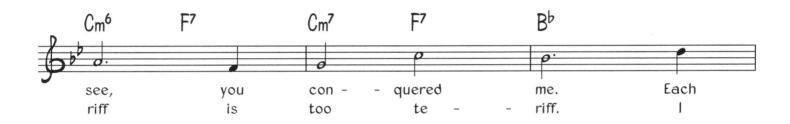

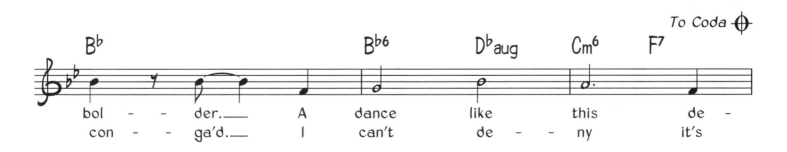

- cha - - cha,_____ when I got - - cha_____

_ in my arms,_____ this_____

_ Cu - ban hot - - cha_____ adds so

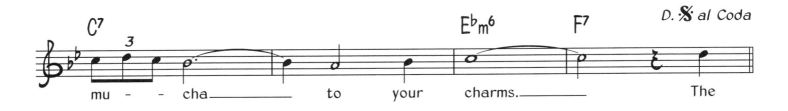

D. $\mathscr{S}$ al Coda

mu - - cha_____ to your charms._____ The

⊕ CODA

got that aye - - yi con - - ga,_____

aye - - yi con - - ga,_____ aye - - yi

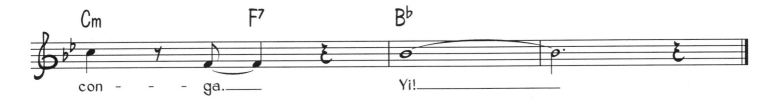

con - - ga._____ Yi!_____

I Found Lovin'
(Medium Disco)

Words & Music by Michael Walker & Johnny Flippin

know that I played the fool. But then you came in -

- to my life and you changed it 'cause I know what I

want and where it's at. I found lov - ing

since I found you, I'm in love with you I found

lov - ing, since I found you, I'm in

love with you, I found lov - in'.

1.

2.

Yeah,
(ad lib.)

Repeat ad lib. to fade

I found some lov - in'. Oh,

I Get Along Without You Very Well
(Foxtrot)

Words & Music by Hoagy Carmichael

should._____ What a guy!_____ What a

fool am I_____ To think my break-ing heart_ could kid the moon;_

_____ What's in store?_____ Should I

phone once more?__ No, it's best that I stick to my

tune._____ I get a-long with - out you ve - ry

well,_____ Of course I do,_____ Ex - cept per - haps in Spring;_

— but I should nev - er think of Spring, For that would sure - ly

break my heart in two._____ two._____

I Hear Music
(Quickstep)

Words by Frank Loesser ★ Music by Burton Lane

I Love You Truly

(Old-Time Waltz)

Words & Music by Carrie Jacobs-Bond

I love you tru - ly, tru - - ly, dear,

Life with its sor - - row, life with its tear,

fades in - to dreams when I feel you are near,

For I love you tru - - ly, tru - - ly dear!

I Remember You
(Foxtrot)

Words by Johnny Mercer ★ Music by Victor Schertzinger

I Will Survive

(Bright Disco)

Words & Music by Dino Fekaris & Freddie Perren

At first I was a-fraid, I was pet - ri - fied;___ kept think - in'

I could nev - er live___ with - out you by my side But then I

spent so ma - ny nights___ think - in' how you did me wrong, and I grew

strong and I learned how to get a - long.___ And so you're back   from out - er space;
me,   some - bo - dy new:___

___ I just walked in to find___ you here___ with that___ sad
___ I'm not that chained up___ lit - tle per - son still in love___

look up - on___your face. I should have changed that stu - pid lock,_ I should have made_
__with you._ And so you feel like drop - pin' in_ and just ex -

134

135

I'd Like To Teach The World To Sing
(Quickstep)

Words & Music by Roger Cook, Roger Greenaway, Bill Backer & Billy Davis

I'd like to build the world a home_ and fur-nish it with love,_ Grow

ap-ple trees and hon-ey bees_ and snow-white tur-tle doves. I'd

like to teach the world to sing_ in per-fect har-mo-ny,____ I'd

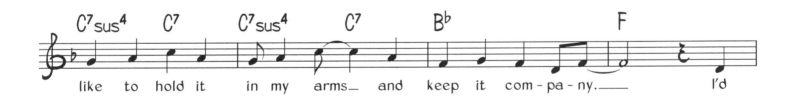

like to hold it in my arms_ and keep it com-pa-ny.___ I'd

To Coda

like to see the world for once_ all stand-ing hand in hand,_ And

hear them ec-ho through the hills___ for peace through-out the land._

_Thats the song I hear;___ let the world sing to - day___ A

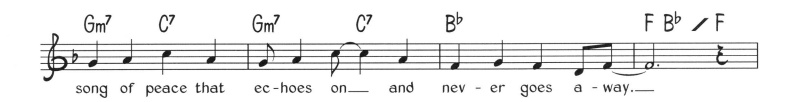

song of peace that ec-hoes on__ and nev - er goes a - way.__

Put your hand in my hand, let's be - gin to - day.

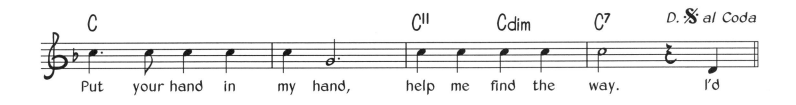

Put your hand in my hand, help me find the way. I'd

CODA

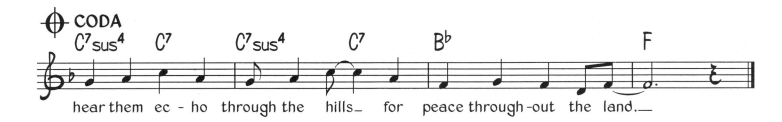

hear them ec - ho through the hills_ for peace through -out the land.__

I'd Do Anything

(Quickstep)

Words & Music by Lionel Bart

I'll Always Be In Love With You

(Waltz)

Words & Music by Herman Ruby, Bud Green & Sam Stept

Sweet - heart if you should stray a mil - lion miles a -
though you find more bliss in some - one el - se's

- way, I'll al - ways be in love with you.
kiss, I'll al - ways be in

And love with you I

can't do an - y more, I've tried so hard to please; But

let me thank you for such ten - der me - mo - ries. I

wish you hap - pi - ness; as for me, sweet-heart, I guess I'll

al - ways be in love with you.

I'll Take You Home Again Kathleen

(Irish - Foxtrot)

Words & Music by Thomas P. Westendorf

If I Had A Talking Picture Of You
(Old-Time Quickstep)

Words & Music by B.G. De Sylva, Lew Brown & Ray Henderson

If I Were A Bell

(Quickstep)

Words & Music by Frank Loesser

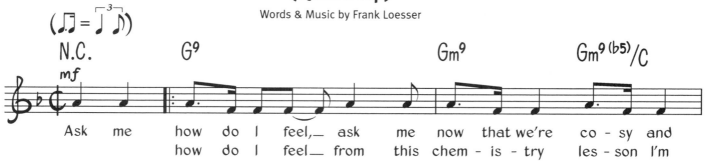

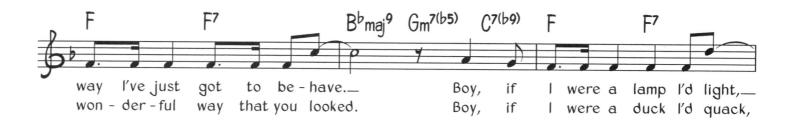

how do I feel,— lit - tle me with my qui - et up - bring - ing.___
how do I feel,— ask me now that we're fond - ly ca - ress - ing.___

— Well sir, all I can say___ is, if I___ were a gate___ I'd be
— Pal, if I were a sa - lad I know___ I'd be splash - ing my

swing - ing.___ And if I were a watch I'd start pop - ping my
dress - ing.___ Or if I were a sea - son I'd sure - ly be

spring,___ Or if I were a bell___ I'd go
Spring,___ Or if I were a bell___ I'd go

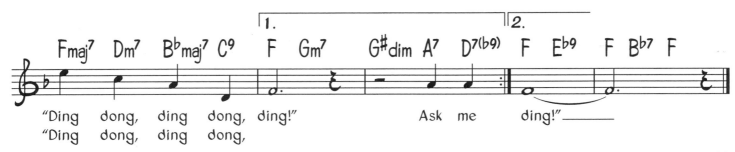

"Ding dong, ding dong, ding!" Ask me ding!"___
"Ding dong, ding dong,

If I Were A Blackbird
(Irish Waltz)

Words & Music by Delia Murphy

1. I am a young maid-en and my sto-ry is

(Verse 2 see block lyric)

sad, For once I was court-ed by a brave sai-lor

lad; He court-ed me tru-ly by night and by

day, But now he has left me and gone far a-

-way. If I were a black-bird, I'd whis-tle and

sing, And I'd fol-low the ship that my true love sails

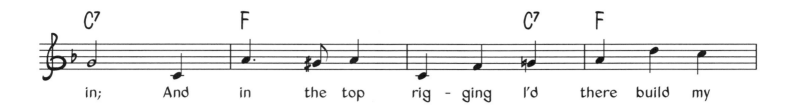

in; And in the top rig - ging I'd there build my

nest, And I'd pil - low my head on his li - ly white breast. *(Instrumental)*

2. His

Verse 2
His parents they chide me and will not agree
That me and my sailor boy married should be,
But let them deride me and do what they will,
While there's breath in my body he's the one I love still.
If I were a blackbird *etc.*

If You're Irish Come Into The Parlour

(Irish Jig)

Words & Music by Shaun Glenville & Frank Miller

If I Had My Way
(Old-Time Waltz)

Words by Lou Klein ★ Music by James Kendis

It's A Long Way To Tipperary
(Irish Reel)

Words & Music by Jack Judge & Harry Williams

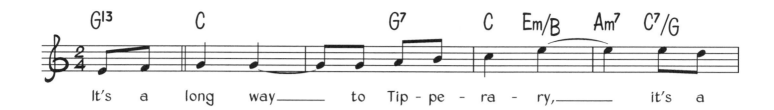

It's a long way____ to Tip - pe - ra - ry,____ it's a

long way____ to go.____ It's a long way____ to Tip - pe -

- ra - ry,____ to the sweet - est girl I know.____

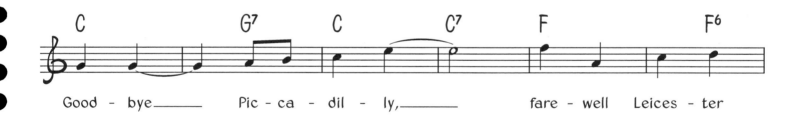

Good - bye____ Pic - ca - dil - ly,____ fare - well Leices - ter

Square!_____ It's a long, long way to Tip - pe - ra - -

- ry, but my heart____ is there.____

The Isle Of Innisfree
(Irish - Foxtrot)

Words & Music by Dick Farrelly

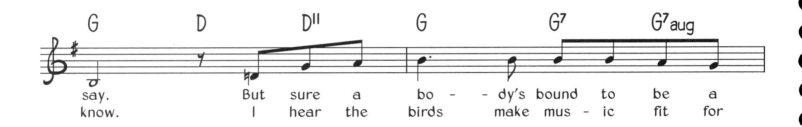

150

sea,   Es - pe - c'lly   when   it   hap - pens   he's   an
- hold   The folks   I   love   a - round   the   turf   fire

ex - ile_____   From   that   dear   love - - ly   Isle   of   In - nis -
gath - ered,_____   On   bend - ed   knees   their   ro - sa - ry   is

- free.   And   when   the   moon - light   peeps   a - cross   the
told.   But dreams don't   last,   tho'   dreams   are   not   for -

roof - tops_____   Of   this   great   ci - - ty,   wond -'rous tho'   it
- got - ten,_____   And   soon   I'm   back   to   stern   re - al - it -

be,   I   scarce - ly   feel   its   won - der   or   its
- y.   But, tho' they   paved   the   foot - ways   here   with

laugh - ter;_____   I'm   once   a - gain   back   home   in   In - nis -
gold   dust,_____   I   still   would   choose   the   Isle   of   In - nis -

1.
- free.
- free.

2.
rit.
2. I   wan - der   - free.

Isn't It Romantic

(Slow Foxtrot)

Words by Lorenz Hart ★ Music by Richard Rodgers

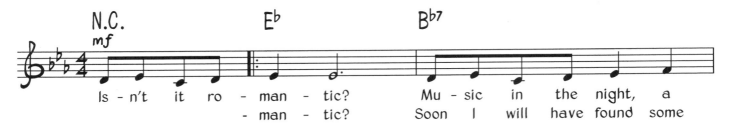

Is - n't it ro - man - tic? Music in the night, a
- man - tic? Soon I will have found some

dream that can be heard. Is - n't it ro - man - tic?
girl that I a - dore. Is - n't it ro - man - tic?

Mov - ing sha - dows write the old - est mag - ic word. I
While I sit a - round, my love can scrub the floor. She'll

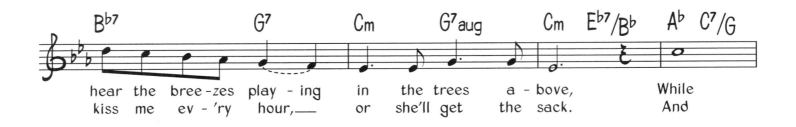

hear the bree - zes play - ing in the trees a - bove, While
kiss me ev - 'ry hour,___ or she'll get the sack. And

all the world is say - ing you were meant for love. Is - n't it ro -
when I take a show - er she can scrub my back. Is - n't it ro -

-man - tic   Mere - ly   to   be   young   on   such   a   night   as
-man - tic?   On   a   moon - light   night   she'll   cook   me   on - ion

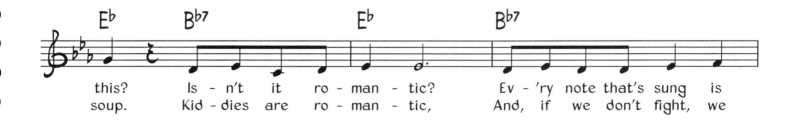

this?   Is - n't   it   ro - man - tic?   Ev - 'ry   note   that's   sung   is
soup.   Kid - dies   are   ro - man - tic,   And,   if   we   don't   fight,   we

like   a   lov - er's   kiss.   Sweet   sym - bols   in   the   moon - light,
soon   will   have   a   troupe!   We'll   help   the   po - pu - la - tion,

Do   you   mean   that   I   will   fall   in   love   per - chance?___
It's   a   du - - ty   that   we   owe   to   dear   old   France.___

___   Is - n't   it   ro - mance?___   Is - n't   it   ro - - mance?___
___   Is - n't   it   ro -

It's A Most Unusual Day

(Waltz)

Words by Harold Adamson ★ Music by Jimmy McHugh

Johnny B. Goode
(Rock 'N' Roll)

Words & Music by Chuck Berry

Deep down in Lou-'si-an-a close to
(Verses 2, 3 see block lyric)

New Or - leans,— 'Way back up in the woods a-mong the ev-er - greens,— There

stood an old cab-in made of earth and wood,— Where lived a coun-try boy named—

John-ny B. Goode,— Who'd nev-er ev-er learned to read or write so well,— But he could

play a gui-tar— just like a - ring-in' a bell.. Go! Go!— Go,—

— John-ny! Go! Go!— Go,— John-ny! Go! Go!— Go,—

Johnny! Go! Go! Go! Johnny! Go! Go!

1. 2.
Johnny B. Goode.

3.
2. He used to
3. His

Verse 2
He used to carry his guitar in a gunny sack,
Go sit beneath the tree by the railroad track;
Ol' engineer in the train sittin' in the shade,
Strummin' with the rhythm that the drivers made.
The people passin' by, they would stop and say,
Oh my but that little country boy could play.
Go! Go! *(etc.)*

Verse 3
His mother told him: "Someday you will be a man,
"And you will be the leader of a big old band;
"Many people comin' from miles around,
"To hear you play your music till the sun goes down.
"Maybe someday your name'll be in lights,
"A-sayin' JOHNNY B. GOODE TONIGHT."
Go! Go! *(etc.)*

Jungle Drums (Canto Karabali)
(Rumba)

Music by Ernesto Lecuona ★ English Words by Carmen Lombardo & Charles O'Flynn

Jun - gle drums,_____ through the black of night,_

Send your mes - sage to me, Bring love's mes - sage to me;_____

_ Guid - ing me_____ through the trop - ic maze,_

With their weird me - lo - dy, Chant - ing their me - lo - dy._____

_ "You are mine"_____ is the mes - sage they cry,_

_ "I am thine_____ long as stars light the sky."

_ Jun - gle drums_____ at your call I fly,_

159

La Bamba

(Samba)

Traditional ★ Adapted & Arranged by Ritchie Valens

(Instrumental)

Pa - ra bai - lar la

bam - ba, Pa - ra bai - lar la la la bam-ba, Se ne - ce -

si u - na po - ca de gra - cia, Un - a po - ca de

gra - cia para me para ti ya a - ri - ba, y'a - ri - ba.

Y'a - ri - ba, y'a - ri - ba, y'a - ri - ba - re por___ ti se -

-re, Por ti se - re.   Bam - ba,   bam -ba,

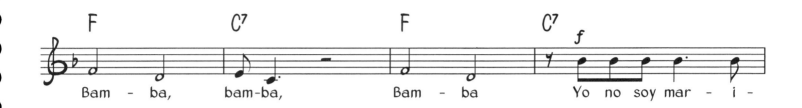

Bam - ba,   bam-ba,   Bam - ba   Yo no soy mar - i -

- ne - ro,   Yo no soy mar - i - ne-ro, Soy cap - i - tan,   Soy_ cap - i -

- tan, Soy cap - i - tan.   Bam - ba,   bam -ba,

Bam - ba,   bam-ba,   Bam - ba,   bam-ba,

Bam - ba.   Pa - ra bai -lar La   Bam - ba._____

The Lambeth Walk
(Old-Time)

Words by Douglas Furber & Arthur Rose ★ Music by Noel Gay

Le Freak
(Medium Disco)

Words & Music by Bernard Edwards & Nile Rodgers

163

Let's All Go Down The Strand
(Old-Time)

Words & Music by Harry Castling & C.W. Murphy

Let's All Sing Like The Birdies Sing
(Old-Time Waltz)

Words by Robert Hargreaves & Stanley J. Damerell ★ Music by Tolchard Evans

Let's all sing like the bird – – ies sing:

Tweet! Tweet! Tweet! Tweet! Tweet!_____

Let's all sing like the bird – – ies sing:

Sweet! Sweet! Sweet! Sweet! Sweet!_____

Let's all war - ble like night – – in - gales,

give your throat a treat._____ Take your

time from the birds, now you all know the words:

Tweet! Tweet! Tweet! Tweet! Tweet!_____

Let's Put It All Together

(Disco Smooch)

Words & Music by Hugo Perreti, Luigi Creatore & George David Weiss

Your arms a-round me are ten-der and warm,— My arms— are meant to
Your lips can thrill me just touch-ing my cheek,— My lips— are meant to

hold you.— Your arms and my arms, } what more is there to say?
kiss you.— Your lips and my lips, }

Let's put it all to-ge-ther.— Let's put it all to-ge-ther,—

let's put it all to-ge-ther, girl, 'Cause lov-in' is all there is.

is. Love like this nev-er hap-pened be-fore,— per-fect— and true,

Day by day we been feel-in' it more,— you love me——— and I love you.

Let's put it all to-ge-ther,— let's put it all to-ge-ther,—

Let's put it all to-ge-ther, girl, 'Cause lov-in' is all there— is.

Lily Of Laguna
(Old-Time)

Words & Music by Leslie Stuart

She's my la-dy love,___ she is my dove, my

ba-by love; she's___ no gal___ for sit-ting down to dream,

she's the on-ly queen La-gu-na knows. I know she

likes me, I know she likes me, be-cause she says so. She is my

Li-ly of La-gu-na, she is my Li-ly and my rose.

Lipstick On Your Collar
(Quickstep)

Words by Edna Lewis ★ Music by George Goehring

When you left me all a - lone at the re - cord hop,_____
You said it be - longed to me,___ made me stop and think;___

Told me you were go - in' out___ for a so - da pop,___
Then I no - ticed yours was red,___ mine was ba - by pink._____

You were gone for quite a while, half an hour or more;___
Who walked in but Ma - ry Jane, lip - stick all a mess!___

You came back and, man oh man, this is what I saw:___
Were you smooch - in' my best friend? Guess the an - swer's yes!___

Lip - stick on your col - lar___ told a tale on you,___

Lip - stick on your col - lar___ said you were un - true;___

Bet your bot - tom dol - lar___ you and I are through, 'Cause

lip - stick on your col - lar___ told a tale on you.

Loch Lomond
(Gay Gordons)

Traditional

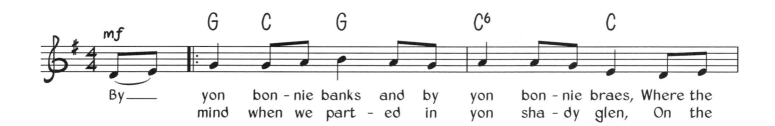

By____ yon bon - nie banks and by yon bon - nie braes, Where the
mind when we part - ed in yon sha - dy glen, On the

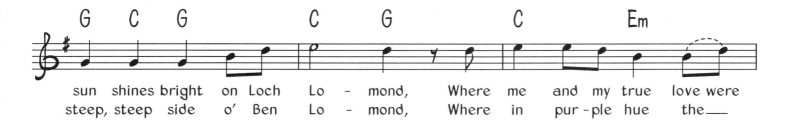

sun shines bright on Loch Lo - mond, Where me and my true love were
steep, steep side o' Ben Lo - mond, Where in pur - ple hue the____

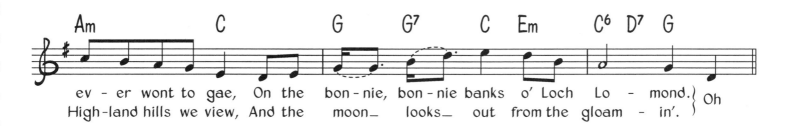

ev - er wont to gae, On the bon - nie, bon - nie banks o' Loch Lo - mond. } Oh
High - land hills we view, And the moon__ looks__ out from the gloam - in'.

ye'll take the high road an' I'll take the low road, An' I'll be in Scot - land a -

- fore ye. But me an' my true love will nev - er meet a - gain on the

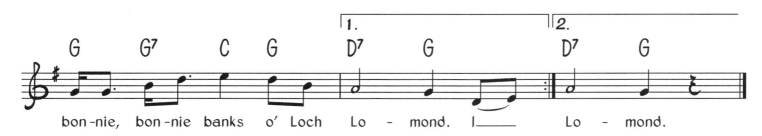

bon - nie, bon - nie banks o' Loch Lo - mond. I____ Lo - mond.

A Lot Of Livin' To Do
(Quickstep)

Words by Lee Adams ★ Music by Charles Strouse

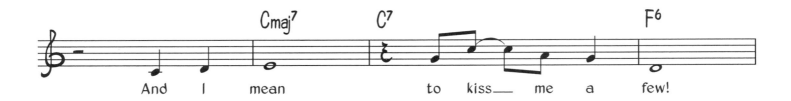

There are girls   just ripe— for some kiss - in',___

And   I   mean   to kiss___ me a   few!

Oh, those   girls   don't know— what they're miss - in';___

I've   got   a   lot   of   liv - in'___   to   do!

And   there's wine   all   read - y   for   tast - in'___

and   there's Cad - il - lacs   all   shi - ny   and   new!

Got - ta   move,   'cause time___ is   a - wast - in'___

There's such a lot of liv - in'___ to do!

There's mu - sic to play,___ pla - ces to go,___ peo - ple to see!___

— Ev - 'ry-thing___ for you and me!___ Life's a

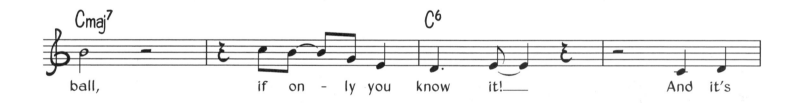

ball, if on - ly you know it!___ And it's

all just wait - in' for you! You're a -

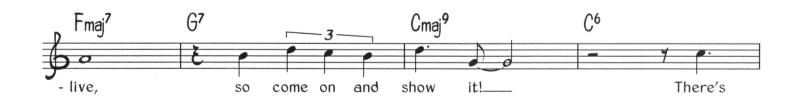

- live, so come on and show it!___ There's

such a lot of liv - in'___ to do!___

171

The Lorelei
(German Waltz)

Traditional

Love From A Heart Of Gold

(Waltz)

Words & Music by Frank Loesser

Where will I find___ a treas - ure___ like the

love from a heart of gold?___ Ev - er

trust - ing and sweet and a - wait - ing my pleas - ure,

rain or shine, Hot or cold,

Wealth far be - yond___ all meas - ure,___ may - be

soon in my hands I'll hold.___ Ah, but

where will I find the one treas - ure of treas - ures, The

love from a heart of gold?___

Love Really Hurts Without You

(Bright Disco)

Words & Music by Les Charles & Ben Findon

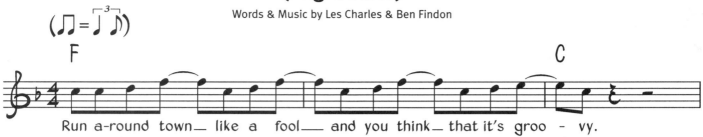

Run a-round town— like a fool— and you think— that it's groo - vy.

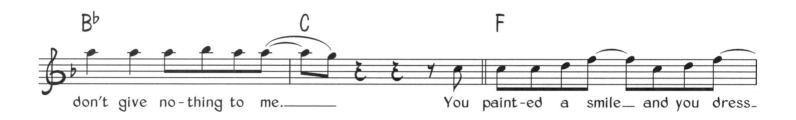

You're giv-ing it to some oth-er guy—— who gives you the eye,—— you

don't give no-thing to me.———— You paint-ed a smile— and you dress—

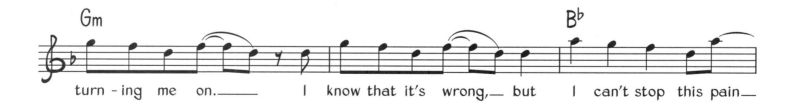

— all the while— to ex-cite— me, but don't you know you're

turn-ing me on.—— I know that it's wrong,— but I can't stop this pain—

— in-side me, ba - by. Love real-ly hurts— with-out you,—

Love's Old Sweet Song
(Old-Time)

Words by Clifton Bingham ★ Music by James Molloy

Lucille
(Rock 'N' Roll)

Words & Music by Albert Collins & Richard Penniman

1. Lu - cille, won't you do your sis-ter's will?___ Oh,___ Lu - cille,___
(Verses 2, 3 see block lyric)

Won't you do your sis-ter's will?___ Well, you ran a-way and left;

1. 2. I___ love you still.___

3. Lu - ___

I

woke up this morn - ing; Lu - cille was not in sight. I asked her friends a-bout her, but

all their lips were tight. Lu - cille,___ please come back where you be - long.___

I been good to you ba-by; Please don't leave me a- lone.___

Verse 2
Lucille, please come back where you belong,
Oh, Lucille,
Please come back where you belong.
I been good to you baby,
Please don't leave me alone.

Verse 3
Lucille, baby satisfy my heart,
Oh, Lucille,
Baby satisfy my heart.
I slaved for you baby,
And gave you such a wonderful start.

Mambo In The Moonlight

(Mambo)

Words & Music by Buddy Kaye & Jules Loman

Mam - bo, mam - bo___ in the moon - light,___ In the moon - light_

it's a thrill! If the moon - light_ does -n't get_ her,_ You can bet the

mam - bo will!___   1. Have you a girl who don't treat you nice,
2. Now there are girls who are ve - ry shy,

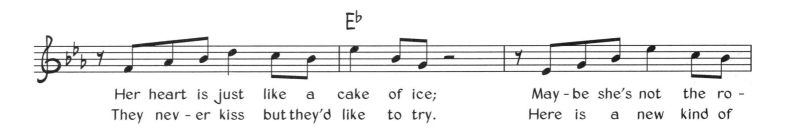

Her heart is just like a cake of ice; May - be she's not the ro -
They nev - er kiss but they'd like to try. Here is a new kind of

- man - tic kind, You can make her change her mind._ Just
re - ci - pe, And it works like T. N. T.___ Just

mam - bo, mam - bo___ in the moon - light,_ In the moon - light_

It's a thrill! If the moon-light_ does-n't get_ her,_ You can bet the

1.
mam - bo will!_

2.
mam - bo will!_

3. You found the girl that you'd
4. Now you can see what the

like to wed,
mam - bo means,
But she wants some - bo - dy else in-stead,
Don't stay at home with your ma - ga-zines.

You'll be the one shop-ping for the ring
You're gon - na find your ro-mance some-how
If you learn to
If you do the

do one thing._ Just}
mam - bo now._ Just}
mam - bo, mam - bo_ in the moon - light,

In the moon - light_ it's a thrill! If the moon - light_

1.   to 4th verse
2.

does-n't get_ her, You can bet the mam-bo will!_
mam-bo will!_

179

Mambo Italiano
(Mambo)

Words & Music by Bob Merrill

A girl went back to Na-po-li Be-cause she missed the scen-er-y, The

na - tive dan -ces and the charm-ing songs___ But, wait a min - ute,

some - thing's wrong; 'Cause now it's Hey, mam - bo! Hey, mam - bo I-ta-li-a-no!

Hey, mam-bo! Mam-bo I-ta li-a-no! Go, go, go, you mixed up Si-ci-li-an-o.
Bang bon-go and throw out the pic-co-li-no.

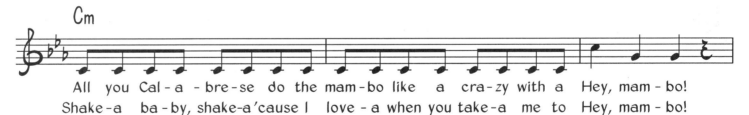

All you Cal-a-bre-se do the mam-bo like a cra-zy with a Hey, mam - bo!
Shake-a ba-by, shake-a 'cause I love - a when you take-a me to Hey, mam - bo!

Don't wan - na ta-ran-tel-la, Hey, mam - bo! No more - a moz-za-rel - la.
Down by the piz-ze-ri - a, Ho, ho, ho, That's where I'm gon-na be - a.

Hey, mam - bo! Mam-bo I-ta - li - an-o! Try an en-cha-la-da with da
No, no, no, Don't tell - a ma-ma mi - a. Ma-ma say "You stop-a or I'm

fish - a - bac - a - lah and then - a Hey, goom - bah!_____ I love - a how you
gon - na tell - a pop - pa." And - a Hey ja - drool,_____ You don't - a have to

dance rum - ba,_____ But take - a some ad - vice, pai - san - o, Learn - a how to mam - bo.
go to school,__ Just make - a wid da beat, bam - bi - no, It's - a like - a vi - no.

If you gon - na be a square, You ain't a - gon - na go no - where.__
Kid, you good - a look - in' but you don't know what's - a cook - in' till you

Hey, mam - bo! Mam - bo I - ta - li - an - o! Hey, mam - bo! Mam - bo I - ta - li - an - o!
Hey, mam - bo! Mam - bo I - ta - li - an - o! Hey, mam - bo! Mam - bo I - ta - li - an - o!

Go, go, Joe. Shake like - a Gi - o - vian - no. Hel - lo, kess - e - deetch, you get - ta
Ho, ho, ho, You mixed up Si - ci - li - a - no. It's - a so de - lish - a, ev - 'ry -

hap - py in the feets a - when you mam - bo_____ I - ta - li -
- bo - dy come ca - pish - a how to mam - bo_____ I - ta - li -

1.
- an - o._____

2.
- an - o._____

181

Maria Elena
(Waltz)

Original Words & Music by Lorenzo Barcelata ★ English Words by Sidney Russell

can't you see how much I care?_____ To

me your voice is like the ech - o of a sigh, And

when you're near my heart can't speak a -bove a sigh. Ma - ri -a E -le -na,

say that we will nev - er part; Ma - ri -a E - le - na,

take me to your heart._____ A

love like mine is great e -nough for two;_____ To share this

love is real -ly all I ask of you._____

Maybellene
(Rock 'N' Roll)

Words & Music by Chuck Berry

May - bel - lene._____ why can't_ you be true?

Oh! May - bel - lene,_____ why can't_ you be true?_____

___ You've start - ed back do - in' the things you used to

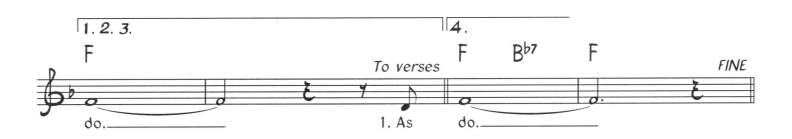

1. 2. 3. | 4.   To verses   FINE

do._____ | 1. As do._____

I was mo - ti - va - tin' ov - er the hill,___ I saw May - bel - lene in a
(Verses 2, 3 see block lyric)

Coup de Ville.___ A Cad - il - lac's a - roll - in' on the o - pen road,_

Noth-in' will out-run my V. 8. Ford.— The Cad-il-lac do-in' 'bout

nine-ty five;— She's bum-per to bum-per, roll-in' side by side.— May-bel-

Verse 2
The Cadillac pulled up ahead of the Ford,
The Ford got hot and wouldn't go no more.
It then got cloudy and started to rain,
I tooted my horn for a passing lane.
The rainwater blowin' all under my hood,
I know that I was do-in' my motor no good.
Maybellene, why can't you be true? *etc.*

Verse 3
The motor cooled down and my heart went down,
And that's when I heard that highway sound.
The Cadillac a-sittin' like a ton of lead,
A Hundred and ten half a mile ahead.
The Cadillac lookin' like it's sittin' still,
And I caught Maybellene at the top o' the hill.
Maybellene, why can't you be true? *etc.*

Memphis Tennessee
(Rock 'N' Roll)

Words & Music by Chuck Berry

mf (Instrumental)

1. Long dis-tance in-for-
(Verses 2, 3, 4, 5 see block lyric)

-ma-tion give me Mem-phis Ten-nes-see,___ Help me find the par-ty try'n' to get in touch with me.___ She could not leave her num-ber but I know who placed the call.___ 'Cos my un-cle took the mes-sage and he wrote it on___ the wall.___

Verse 2
Help me information get in touch with my Marie,
She's the only one who'd phone me here from Mephis Tennessee.
Her home is on the south side, high upon a ridge,
Just a half a mile from the Mississippi Bridge.

Verse 3
(Instrumental)

Verse 4
Help me information, more than that I cannot add,
Only that I miss her and all the fun we had;
But we were pulled apart because her mom did not agree,
And tore apart our happy home in Memphis Tennessee.

Verse 5
The last time I saw Marie she's waving me goodbye,
With hurry-home drops on her cheek that trickled from her eye.
Marie is only six years old; information, please,
Try to put me through to her in Memphis Tennessee.

Mexican Hat Dance (Chiapanecas)

(Novelty)

Traditional

More Than A Woman
(Medium Disco)

Words & Music by Barry Gibb, Robin Gibb & Maurice Gibb

Girl, I've known you ve - ry well, I've seen you grow-ing ev -'ry day;__ I

nev - er real - ly looked be - fore, but now you take_ my breath a - way.

Sud - den - ly you're in my life, part of ev - 'ry-thing I do. You've

got me work - ing day and night, just tryin' to keep a hold on you.

Here in your arms_ I've found my pa - ra - dise,__

my on - ly chance for hap - pi - ness,__ and if I lose you now, I

think I would die.__ Oh say you'll al-ways be my ba - by, we can make it shine.

The Mountains Of Mourne

(Irish Waltz)

Words & Music by Percy French & Houston Collisson

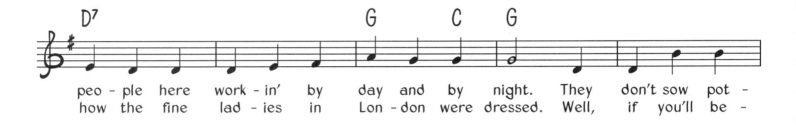

1. Oh Ma - ry, this Lon - don's a won - der - ful sight, Wid the
- lieve that, when writ - in', a wish you ex - pressed As to

(Verses 3, 4, 5 see block lyric)

peo - ple here work - in' by day and by night. They don't sow pot -
how the fine lad - ies in Lon - don were dressed. Well, if you'll be -

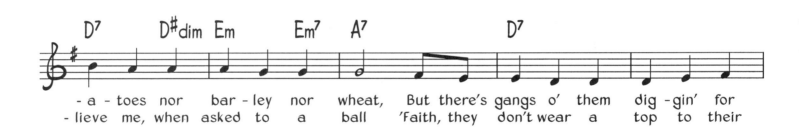

- a - toes nor bar - ley nor wheat, But there's gangs o' them dig - gin' for
- lieve me, when asked to a ball 'Faith, they don't wear a top to their

gold in the street. At____ least when I axed them that's what I was
dres - ses at all. Oh, I've seen them me - self, and you could not, in

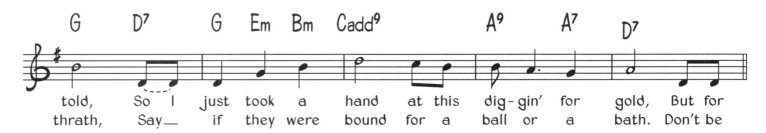

told, So I just took a hand at this dig - gin' for gold, But for
thrath, Say___ if they were bound for a ball or a bath. Don't be

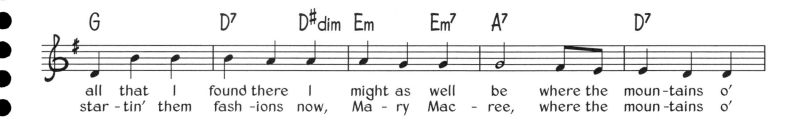

all that I found there I might as well be where the moun-tains o'
star-tin' them fash-ions now, Ma - ry Mac - ree, where the moun-tains o'

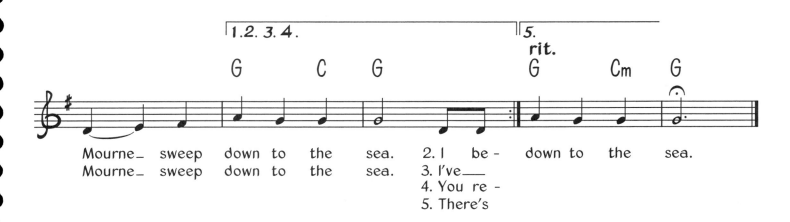

Mourne_ sweep down to the sea. 2. I be - down to the sea.
Mourne_ sweep down to the sea. 3. I've___
4. You re -
5. There's

Verse 3
I've seen England's king from the top of a bus;
I never knew him, tho' he means to know us.
And, tho' by the Saxon we once were oppressed,
Still I cheered (God forgive me!), I cheered with the rest.
And, now that he's visited Erin's green shore,
We'll be much better friends than we've been heretofore.
When we've got all we want, we're as quiet as can be
Where the mountains o' Mourne sweep down to the sea.

Verse 4
You remember young Peter O'Loughlin, of course?
Well, now he is here at the head of the force.
I met him today, I was crossin' the Strand,
And he stopped the whole street wid wan wave of his hand.
And there we stood talkin' of days that are gone,
While the whole population of London looked on.
But, for all these great powers, he's wishful, like me,
To be back where dark Mourne sweeps down to the sea.

Verse 5
There's beautiful girls here – oh, nivver you mind! –
Wid beautiful shapes nature niver designed
And lovely complexions, all roses and crame;
But O'Loughlin remarked, wid regard to the same,
That "If those roses you venture to sip,
The colours might all come away on your lip."
So I'll wait for the wild rose that's waitin' for me
Where the mountains o' Mourne sweep down to the sea.

Mull Of Kintyre
(Waltz)

Words & Music by Paul McCartney & Denny Laine

Mull__ of Kin - tyre, Oh mist roll - ing in from__ the

sea, my de - sire is al - ways to be here, Oh

Mull__ of Kin - tyre!

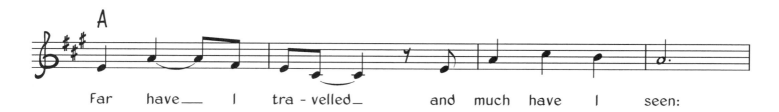

Far have__ I tra - velled__ and much have I seen:

Dark dis - tant moun - tains__ with val - leys__ of green,

Past paint - ed des - serts,__ the sun - set's on fire__ as he car -

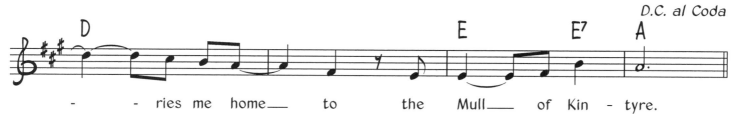

- - ries me home__ to the Mull__ of Kin - tyre.

CODA

Sweep through the hea-ther like deer in the glen, Car-ry me back to the days I knew then; Nights when we sang like a hea-ven-ly choir of the life and the times of the Mull of Kin-tyre. Mull of Kin-tyre, Oh mist roll-ing in from the sea, my de-sire is al-ways to be here, Oh Mull of Kin-tyre!

My Kind Of Town (Chicago Is)
(Quickstep)

Words by Sammy Cahn ★ Music by Jimmy Van Heusen

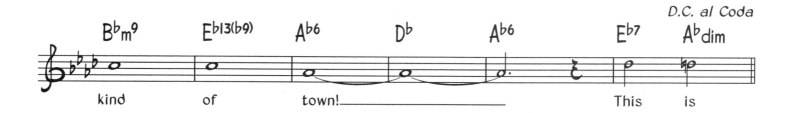

D.C. al Coda

kind of town!_____ This is

the Wrig - ley Build - ing; Chi - ca - go is

the Win - dy Ci - ty; Chi - ca - go is

the Un - ion Stock - yards; Chi - ca - go is

Com - is - key Ball - park; Chi - ca - go is

one town that won't let you down,___ It's my___

___ kind of town!_____

195

My Love
(Quickstep)

Words & Music by Tony Hatch

My love is warm-er than the warm-est sun-shine,

soft-er than a sigh;___ My love is deep-er than the

deep-est___ o-cean, wi-der than the sky.___ My love is

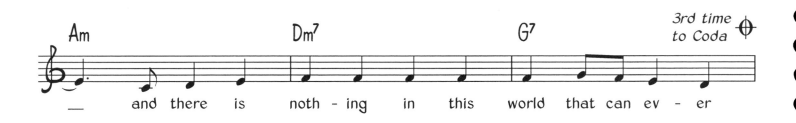

bright-er than the bright-est___ star that shines ev-'ry night a-bove,___

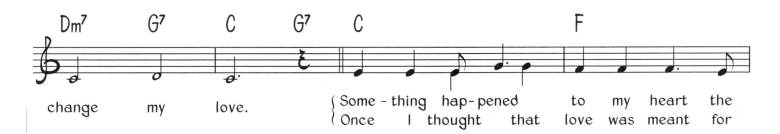

_ and there is noth-ing in this world that can ev-er

change my love. { Some-thing hap-pened to my heart the
{ Once I thought that love was meant for

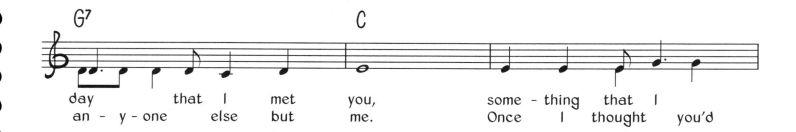

day | that I | met | you, | | some - thing | that I
an - y - one | else | but | me. | Once | I | thought | you'd

nev - er | felt | be - | fore._____ | | You | are | al - ways
nev - er | come | my | way._____ | | Now | it | on - ly

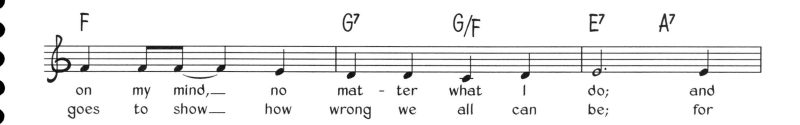

on | my | mind,_ | no | mat - ter | what | I | do; | and
goes | to | show_ | how | wrong | we | all | can | be; | for

ev - 'ry | day_ | it | seems | I | want | you | more. | | My | love | is
now | I | have_ | to | tell | you | ev - 'ry | day:

CODA

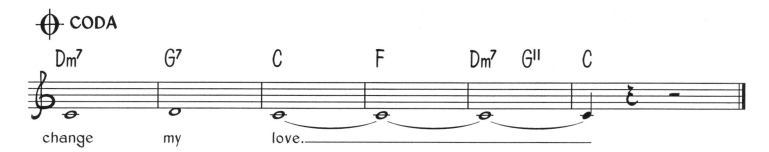

change | my | love._____

My Love She's But A Lassie Yet
(Scottish Reel)

Traditional ★ Words by Robert Burns

My__ love, she's but a lass-ie yet, my__ love, she's but a

lass-ie yet, we'll__ let her stand a year or twa, she'll no__ be__ half sae

sau-cy yet. 1. I__ rue the day I sought her, Oh! I__ rue the day I

(Verses 2, 3 see block lyric)

sought her, Oh! Wha__ gets her need-na say he's woo'd, but he__ may say he's

bought her. Oh! My__ think-in' o't. My__ love, she's but a lass-ie yet, my__

love, she's but a lass-ie yet, we'll— let her stand a

year or twa, she'll no— be— half sae sau - cy yet.

Verse 2
Came draw a drap o' the best o't yet
Came draw a drap o' the best o't yet!
Gae seek for pleasure where ye will
But here I never missed it yet
Chorus

Chorus
My love, she's but a lassie yet
My love, she's but a lassie yet!
We'll let her stand a year or twa
She'll no be half sae saucy yet!

Verse 3
We're a' dry wi' drinkin' o't
We're a' dry wi' drinkin' o't!
The minister kiss't the fiddler's wife
He couldna preach for thinkin' o't!
Chorus

My Wild Irish Rose
(Irish Waltz)

Words & Music by Chauncey Olcott

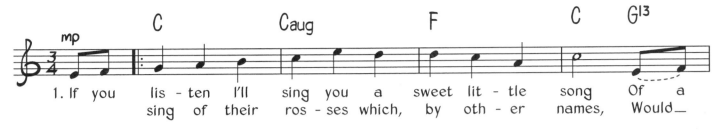

1. If you lis - ten I'll sing you a sweet lit - tle song, Of a
sing of their ros - ses which, by oth - er names, Would

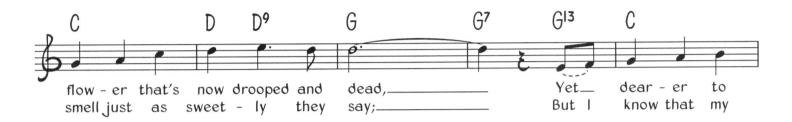

flow - er that's now drooped and dead,_____ Yet_ dear - er to
smell just as sweet - ly they say;_____ But I know that my

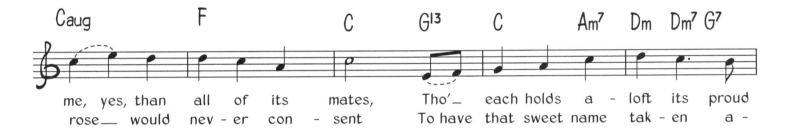

me, yes, than all of its mates, Tho'_ each holds a - loft its proud
rose_ would nev - er con - sent To have that sweet name tak - en a -

head._____ 'Twas giv - en to me by a girl that I
- way._____ Her glan - ces are shy when - e'er I pass

know. Since we've met, faith, I've known no re - pose._____ She is
by The_ bow - er where my true love grows._____ And my

dear - er by far than the world's bright - est star, And I call her my
one wish has been that some day I may win The_ heart of my

Mona Lisa
(Slow Foxtrot)

Words & Music by Jay Livingston & Ray Evans

Mo - na Li - sa, Mo - na Li - sa men have named you, You're so

like the la-dy with the mys-tic smile, Is it on - ly 'cause you're lone -ly___ they have

blamed you For that Mo - na Li - sa strange-ness___ in your smile? Do you

smile to tempt a lov - er,___ Mo - na Li - sa?___ Or is this your way to hide a bro-ken

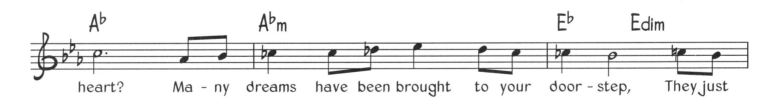

heart? Ma - ny dreams have been brought to your door - step, They just

lie there, and they die there. Are you warm, are you real, Mo - na

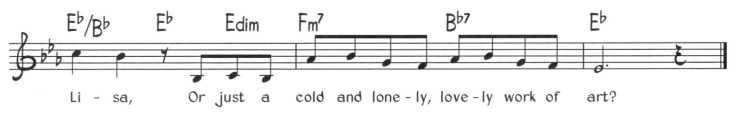

Li - sa, Or just a cold and lone - ly, love - ly work of art?

No Particular Place To Go
(Rock 'N' Roll)

Words & Music by Chuck Berry

Ri - ding a - long in my au - to - mo - bile,   My ba - by be - side me at the
(Verses 2, 3, 4 see block lyric)

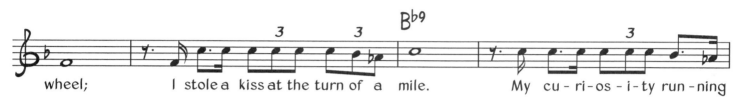

wheel;   I stole a kiss at the turn of a mile.   My cu - ri - os - i - ty run - ning

wild;   Cruis - ing and play - ing the ra - di - o,   With no par - tic - u - lar place to

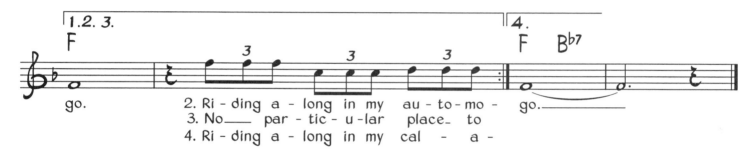

go.   2. Ri - ding a - long in my au - to - mo - go.
3. No___ par - tic - u - lar   place_ to
4. Ri - ding a - long in my cal - a -

Verse 2
Riding along in my automobile,
I was anxious to tell her the way I feel;
So I told her softly and sincere,
And she leaned and whispered in my ear;
Cuddling more and driving slow,
With no particular place to go.

Verse 3
No particular place to go,
So we parked way out on the cocamo;
The night was young and the moon was gold,
So we both decided to take a stroll.
Can you imagine the way I felt?
I couldn't unfasten my safety belt!

Verse 4
Riding along in my calaboose,
Still trying to get the belt unloose;
All the way home I held a grudge,
For the safety belt that wouldn't budge;
Cruising and playing the radio,
With no particular place to go.

203

Night Fever
(Medium Disco)

Words & Music by Barry Gibb, Robin Gibb & Maurice Gibb

Lis - ten to__ the ground, there is move - ment all__ a - round, there is

some - thing go - ing down and I can feel it. On the

waves of__ the air, there is danc - ing out__ there,_ if it's

some - thing we can share, we can steal it. And that

sweet ci - ty wo - man, she moves through the light,__ con -

- troll - ing my mind__ and my soul.__ When you reach out for me,__ yeah, and the

An Old Fashioned Love Song
(Quickstep)

Words & Music by Paul Williams

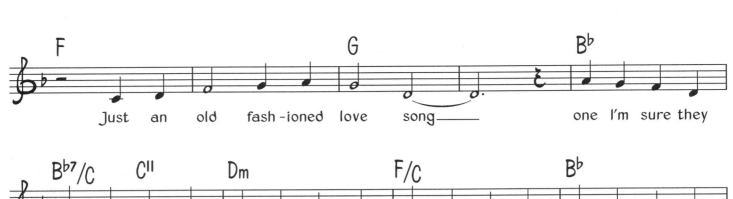

Just an old fash-ioned love song _____ one I'm sure they

wrote for you and me to weave our dreams up-on and lis-ten to each

eve-'ning when the lights are low. _____

To un-der-score our love af-fair with ten-der-ness and

D. %: al Coda

feel-ings that we've come to know. _____

⊕ CODA

Repeat to fade

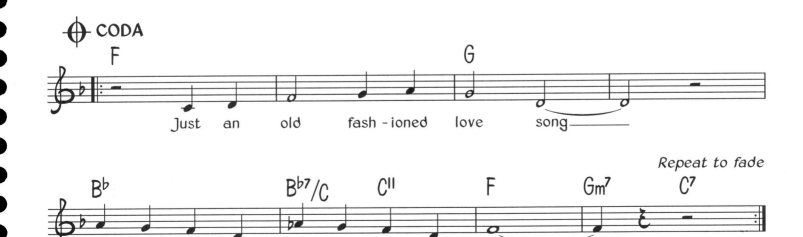

Just an old fash-ioned love song _____

com-ing down in three-part har-mo-ny. _____

One, Two, Button Your Shoe
(Quickstep)

Words by Johnny Burke ★ Music by Arthur Johnston

I've found a use for Mo-ther Goose that well de-serves my

praise,___ It's been such a con-so-la-tion when you start your tar-dy

ways. When we've a date, I'm nev-er late, You're nev-er quite on

time.___ So I made a va-ri-a-tion on an old fa-mi-liar rhyme:

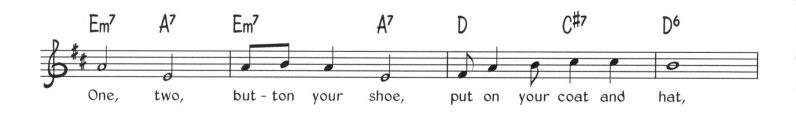

One, two, but-ton your shoe, put on your coat and hat,

I play a game like that while I'm wait-ing for you.

Three, four, o-pen the door, hur-ry for heav-en's sake;

I count each step you take while I'm wait - ing for you.

Five, six, my heart does tricks as I pic - ture all your charms,

Sev - en, eight, you're at the gate, and you walk in - to my arms.

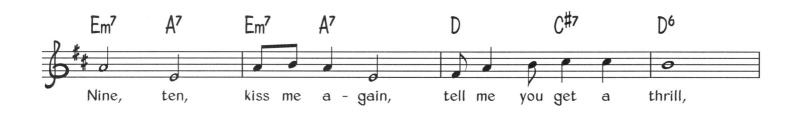

Nine, ten, kiss me a - gain, tell me you get a thrill,

Just as I hope you will, while I'm wait - ing for you.

Oh! Oh! Antonio
(Old-Time Waltz)

Words & Music by C.W. Murphy & Dan Lipton

P.S. I Love You
(Foxtrot)

Words by Johnny Mercer ★ Music by Gordon Jenkins

Parade Of The Wooden Soldiers
(Old-Time)

Music by Leon Jessel ★ English Words by Ballard MacDonald

The toy - shop door is locked up tight and
dolls are in their best ar - rayed, there's

ev - 'ry - thing is qui - et for the night, When sud - den - ly the
going to be a won - der - ful pa - rade. Hark to the drum. Oh!

1.
clock strikes twelve, the fun's be - gun. The

2.
Here they come, cries ev - 'ry -

- one.

Hear them all cheer - ing, Now they are near - ing,

There's the cap - tain stiff as starch; Ba - yo - nets flash - ing,

Mu - sic is crash - ing, As the wood - en sol - diers march,

Sa - bres a - clink - ing, sol - diers a - wink - ing At each pret - ty

lit - tle maid. Here they come! Here they come! Here they come! Here they come!

Wood - en sol - diers on pa - rade. Day - light is creep - ing,

Dol - lies are sleep - ing In the toy shop win - dow fast;

Sol - diers so jol - ly Think of each dol - ly, Dream - ing of the

night that's past. When in the morn - ing, with - out a warn - ing,

Toy - man pulls the win - dow shade, There's no sign the

Wood bri - gade was ev - er out up - on pa - rade.

Peggy Sue
(Rock 'N' Roll)

Words & Music by Buddy Holly, Norman Petty & Jerry Allison

Peg - gy,_____ my Peg - gy Sue!_____

Oh well, I

love you, gal;_____ and I need you, Peg - gy Sue._____

I love you,_____ Peg - gy Sue,_____

With a love so rare and true._____ Oh,

Peg - gy,_____ my Peg - gy Sue!_____

Oh well, I

love you gal;_____ yes, I want you,

Peg - gy Sue!_____

The Petite Waltz (La Petite Valse)
(Waltz)

Words by Duke Ellington & Phyllis Claire ★ Music by Joe Heyne

Phil The Fluter
(Irish Reel)

Words & Music by Percy French

1. Have you heard of Phil the flu - ter who would nev - er pay the rent? When -
(Verses 2, 3 see block lyric)

-ev - er he was down and out, with - out a sin - gle cent, He would

cir - cu - late a no - tice to his neigh - bours one and all As to

how he'd like their com - pa - ny that eve - ning at a ball. And,

when writ - in' out, he was care - ful to sug - gest to them That,

if they found a hat of his con - ven - ient to the door, The

more they put in_____ when - ev - er he re - quest - ed them, The

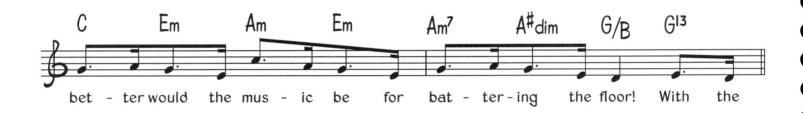
bet - ter would the mus - ic be for bat - ter - ing the floor! With the

toot of the flute and the twid - dle of the fid - dle, O!

Hop - ping in the mid - dle like a her - ring on the grid - dle, O!

Up, down, hands a - round, cross - in' to the wall.___ So

come and join the gai – e - ty at Phil the flu - ter's ball!

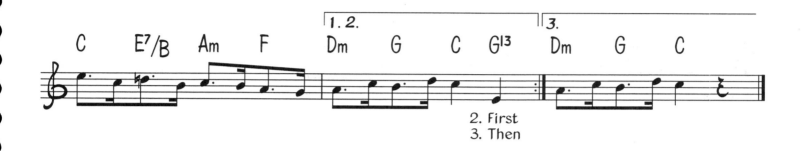

2. First
3. Then

Verse 2
First little Mickey Mulligan got up to show them how.
And then the widow Cafferty steps out and makes her bow.
"I could dance you off your legs," says she, "as sure as you were born,
If you'll only make the piper play 'Hare Is In The Corn'."
So Phil plays up to the best of his ability,
The lady and the gentleman begin to do their share.
While young Mick was aprancin' with agility,
Decrepit Missus Cafferty was leapin' like a hare!

Verse 3
Then Phil the fluter tipped a wink to little crooked Pat.
"I think it's nearly time." says he, "for passin' round the hat."
So Paddy does the necessary, looking mighty cute.
Says "Ye've got to pay the piper when he toothers on the flute."
Then all joined in wid the greatest joviality,
Covering the Buckle and the Shuffle and the Trent.
Jigs were danced of the very finest quality.
The widow found a husband and the fluter found the rent!

A Picture Of You

(Quickstep)

Words & Music by Johnny Beveridge & Peter Oakman

In the night___ there are sights to be seen,___
On a street - -car or in a ca-fe,___

Stars shine like jewels on the crown of a queen;___
All of the ev - 'ning and most of the day,___ My

But the on - ly sight I want to view,___ Is that
mind is in a maze, What can I do?___ I

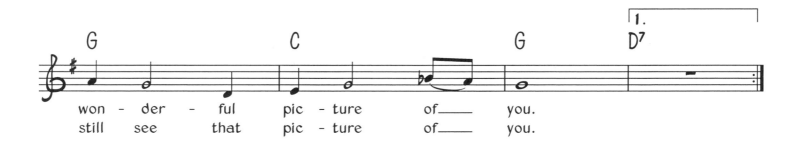

won - der - ful pic - ture of___ you.
still see that pic - ture of___ you.

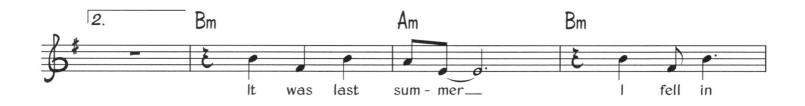

It was last sum - mer___ I fell in

love, My heart told me what to do.___

220

I saw you there on the crest of a

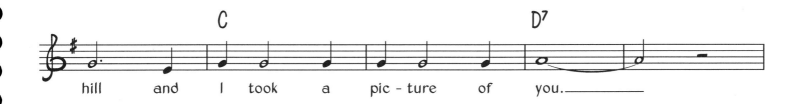

hill and I took a pic - ture of you.____

Then you were gone____ like a dream in the night,____

With you went my heart my love____ and my life.____ I

did-n't know your name what could I do?____ I

on - ly had a pic - ture of____ you._____

Portrait Of My Love

(Foxtrot)

Words by David West ★ Music by Cyril Ornadel

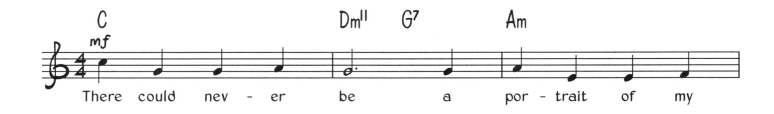

There could nev - er be a por - trait of my

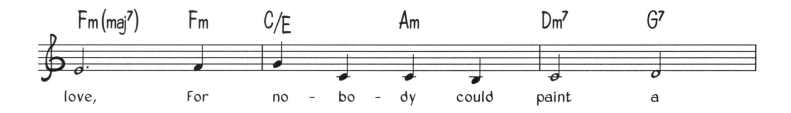

love, For no - bo - dy could paint a

dream._____ You will nev - er see a

por - trait of my love, For mi - ra - cles are

nev - er seen._____ An - - y one who

sees her_____ soon_____ for - gets the

Mo - na Li - - sa. It would take, I know, a

Mi - chel - an - ge - lo, And he would need the glow of dawn that

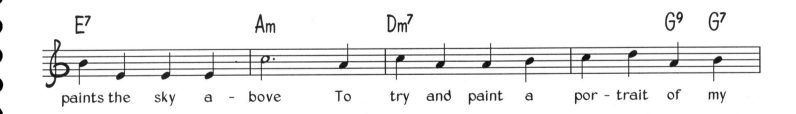

paints the sky a - bove To try and paint a por - trait of my

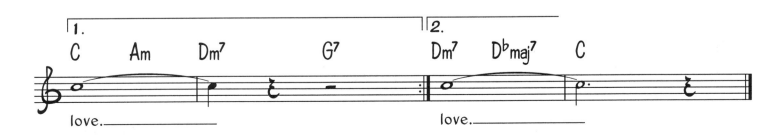

love._____ love._____

Put On A Happy Face
(Quickstep)

Words by Lee Adams ★ Music by Charles Strouse

Grey skies are gon - na clear up,— put on a hap - py face,

Brush off the clouds and cheer up,— put on a hap - py face.

Take off the gloo - my mask of tra - ge-dy, it's not your style;

You'll look so good that you'll be glad ya' de - cid - ed to smile.—

Pick out a pleas -ant out-look,— stick out that no - ble chin;

Wipe off that "full of doubt" look,— slap on a hap - py grin! And

spread sun - shine all ov - er the place. Just

put on a hap - py face!—

Rasputin
(Bright Disco)

Words & Music by Frank Farian, George Reyam & Fred Jay

There

lived a cer-tain man in Rus-sia long a-go. He was big and strong in his

eyes a flam-ing glow. Most peo-ple looked at him with ter-ror and fear but to

Mos-cow chicks he was such a love-ly dear. He could preach the

Bi-ble like a preach-er, full of ec-sta-sy and fire.

But he al-so was the kind of teach-er wo-men would de-sire.

Ra - ra - ras-pu-tin, lov-er of the Rus-sian Queen, there was a cat that

real-ly was gone.__ Ra - ra - ras-pu-tin. Rus-sia's great-est love ma-chine.

1.
It was a shame how he car-ried on.__

2.
he car-ried on.__

225

Rave On
(Rock 'N' Roll)

Words & Music by Sunny West, Bill Tilghman & Norman Petty

The lit - tle things_ you say and do,____ They
way you dance_ and hold me tight,____ The

make me want to be with you - hoo -hoo. } Rave on! It's a
way you kiss and say good - ni - ni -night! }

cra - zy feel - in', And I know it's___ got me reel - in' when

you say: "I love___ you."___ Rave on!___

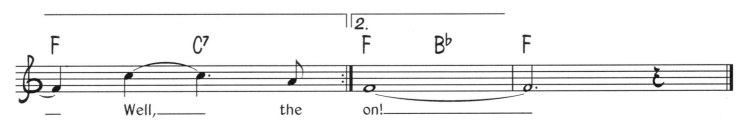

_ Well,____ the on!____

Reelin' And Rockin'
(Rock 'N' Roll)

Words & Music by Chuck Berry

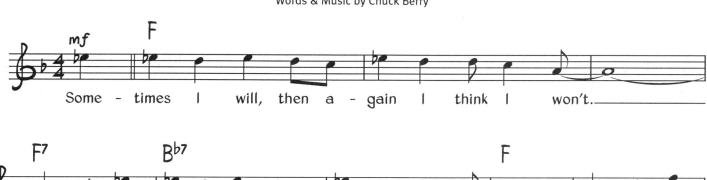

Some - times I will, then a - gain I think I won't.____

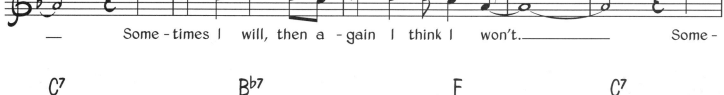

__ Some - times I will, then a - gain I think I won't.____ Some -

- times I do, then a - gain I____ think I don't.____ Well, I

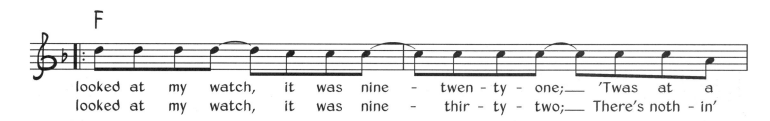

looked at my watch, it was nine - twen - ty - one;____ 'Twas at a
looked at my watch, it was nine - thir - ty - two;____ There's noth - in'

rock 'n' roll dance, hav - in' noth - in' but fun.____ We were roll - in',____
I'd____ rather do than____ dance with you.____ We were roll - in',____

Reel - in' and a - rock - in'.____ We were reel - in' and a-rock - in' and roll-

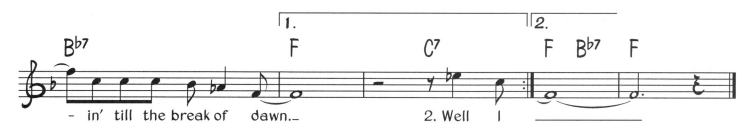

- in' till the break of dawn.__ 2. Well I _____

Release Me

(Foxtrot)

Words & Music by Eddie Miller, Dub Williams & Robert Yount

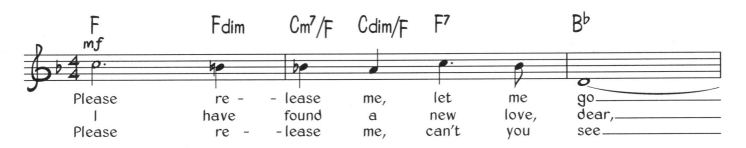

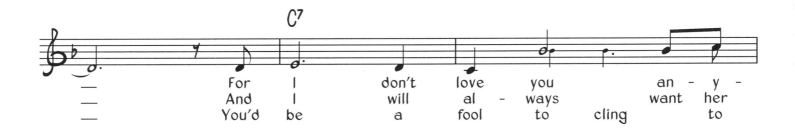

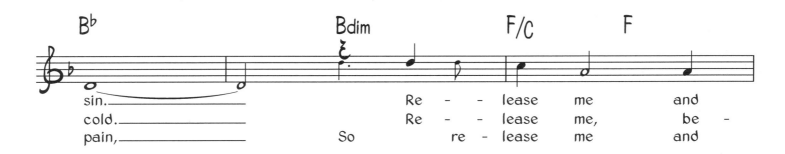

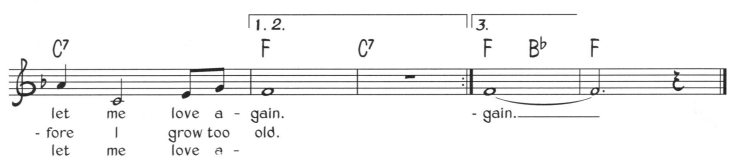

Ring My Bell
(Medium Disco)

Words & Music by Frederick Knight

Rock And Roll Music

(Rock 'N' Roll)

Words & Music by Chuck Berry

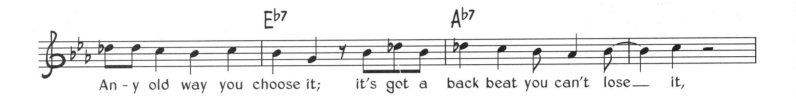

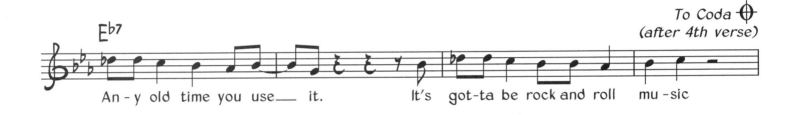

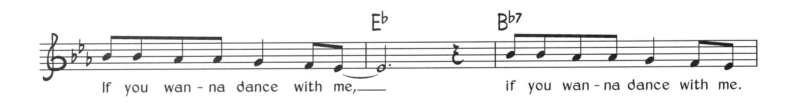

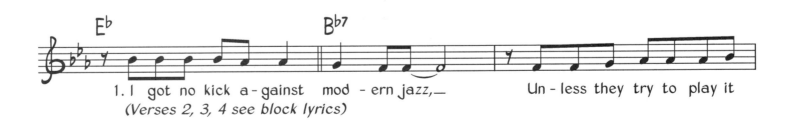

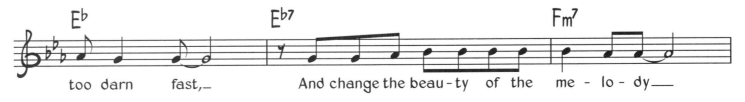

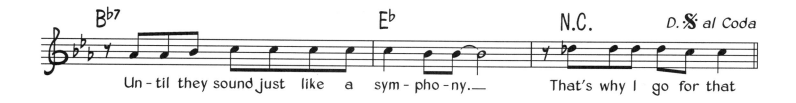

Un - til they sound just like a sym - pho - ny.— That's why I go for that

If you wan - na dance with me,— if you wan - na dance with me.—

Verse 2
I took my loved one over 'cross the tracks
So she can hear my man a-wail a sax.
I must admit they have a rockin' band;
Man they were goin' like a hurricane!
That's why I go for that rock and roll music *(etc.)*

Verse 3
Way down South they gave a jubilee;
The jokey folks that had a jamboree,
They're drinkin' home brew from a water cup.
The folks dancin' got all shook up
And started playin' that rock and roll music *(etc.)*

Verse 4
Don't care to hear 'em play a tango,
I'm in the mood to hear a mambo.
It's way too early for a congo,
So keep a-rockin' that piano,
So I can hear some of that rock and roll music *(etc.)*

Rock Around The Clock
(Rock 'N' Roll)

Words & Music by Max C. Freedman & Jimmy De Knight

One, two, three o'- clock, four o'-clock rock, Five, six, sev-en o'-clock

eight o'-clock rock, Nine, ten, e-lev-en o'-clock, twelve o'-clock rock; We're gon-na

rock a-round the clock to-night.__ 1. Put your glad rags on and join me, Hon,__ We'll
(Verses 2, 3, 4, 5 see block lyric)

have some fun when the clock strikes one.__ We're gon-na rock a-round the

clock to-night,__ We're gon-na rock, rock, rock till broad day-light;__ We're gon-na

rock,   gon - na   rock   a - round___ the   clock___ to - night.___

— 2. When the

Verse 2
When the clock strikes two, and three and four,
If the band slows down we'll yell for more.
We're gonna rock around the clock tonight,
We're gonna rock, rock, rock till broad daylight;
We're gonna rock, gonna rock around the clock tonight.

Verse 3
When the chimes ring five and six and seven,
We'll be rockin' up in seventh heav'n.
We're gonna rock around the clock tonight,
We're gonna rock, rock, rock till broad daylight;
We're gonna rock, gonna rock around the clock tonight.

Verse 4
When it's eight, nine, ten, eleven too,
I'll be goin' strong and so will you.
We're gonna rock around the clock tonight,
We're gonna rock, rock, rock till broad daylight;
We're gonna rock, gonna rock around the clock tonight.

Verse 5
When the clock strikes twelve, we'll cool off, then
Start a-rockin' 'round the clock again.
We're gonna rock around the clock tonight,
We're gonna rock, rock, rock till broad daylight;
We're gonna rock, gonna rock around the clock tonight.

Rock-A-Beatin' Boogie
(Rock 'N' Roll)

Words & Music by Bill Haley

Take a rock! take a beat! take a

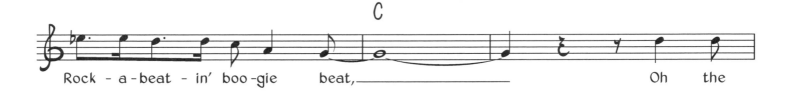

boo-gie! And make it sweet! You get a rock-a-beat-in' boo-gie,

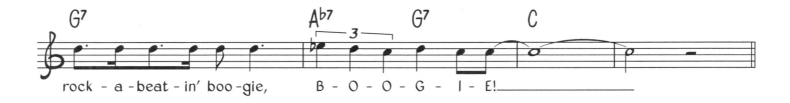

Rock-a-beat-in' boo-gie beat,_____ Oh the

rock-a-beat-in' boo-gie, B-O-O-G-I-E!_____

Danc-ing to the rhy-thm of the rock-a-beat-in' boo-gie,

Rock-in' to the rhy-thm of the rock-a-beat-in' boo-gie,

Shak-in' to the rhy-thm of the rock-a-beat-in' boo-gie,

Jump - in' to the rhy - thm of the rock - a - beat - in' boo - gie,

Shim - my to the rhy - thm of the rock - a - beat - in' boo - gie,

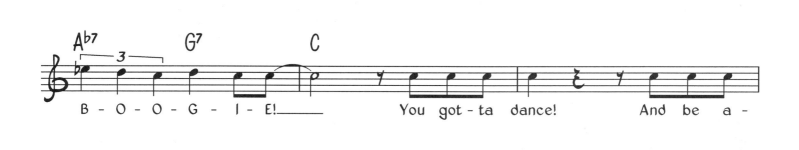

B - O - O - G - I - E! You got - ta dance! And be a -

- live! You got - ta jump, You got - ta jive! To the

rock - a - beat - in' boo - gie, rock - a - beat - in' boo - gie beat,

Oh the rock - a - beat - in' boo - gie,

B - O - O - G - I - E!

Rock Your Baby
(Medium Disco)

Words & Music by Harry Casey & Richard Finch

Wo - - man, take me in your arms,___
rock your ba - - by.___ Wo - - man,

take me in your arms,___ rock your ba - - by.___ *Fine*

There's noth - in' to___ it; just say___ you wan - na do
Yeah, hold me tight___ with___ all your

___ it. O - pen up your heart
___ might, now let your lov - in' flow

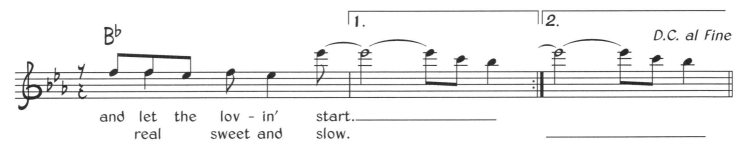

and let the lov - in' start.___
real sweet and slow.

1. 2. *D.C. al Fine*

Roll Over Beethoven
(Rock 'N' Roll)

Words & Music by Chuck Berry

Gon-na write a lit-tle let-ter, gon-na mail it to my lo-cal D. J.

Yes, it's a jump-in' lit-tle re-cord I want my jock-ey to play.

Roll ov - er Beet-ho - ven, I got-ta hear it a-gain to day.

You know my tem-p'ra-ture's ris - in' and the juke box is blow-in' a fuse.

My heart's beat-in' rhy-thm and my soul keeps a-sing-in' the blues.

Roll ov - er Beet-ho - ven and tell Tchai-kov - sky the news.

I got the rock-in' pneu-mo-nia, I need a shot of rhy-thm and blues.

I caught the roll-in' ar-thri-tis, sit-tin' down at a rhy-thm re-view.

Roll ov-er Beet-ho-ven, they're rock-in' in two by two.

Well if you feel you like it, go get your lov-er, Then reel and rock it,

roll it ov-er, Then move on up just a tri-fle fur-ther, Then reel and rock with

one an-oth-er. Roll ov-er Beet-ho-ven, dig these rhy-thm and blues.

Well, it's ear-ly in the morn-in' and I'm giv-in' you my warn-in', Don't you

238

The Rose Of Tralee
(Irish Waltz)

Words & Music by C. Mordaunt Spencer & Charles Glover

Scotland The Brave
(Gay Gordons)

Traditional

See You Later, Alligator
(Rock 'N' Roll)

Words & Music by Robert Guidry

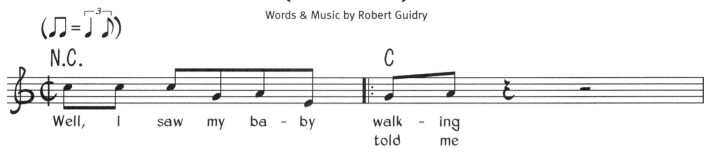

Well, I saw my ba-by walk-ing with a-no-ther man to-day.___
told me near-ly made me lose my head.___

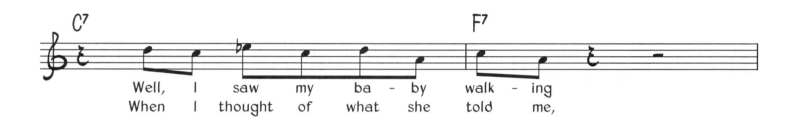

Well, I saw my ba-by walk-ing with a-no-ther man to-day.___
When I thought of what she told me, near-ly made me lose my head.___

When I asked her what's the mat-ter,
But the next time that I saw her,

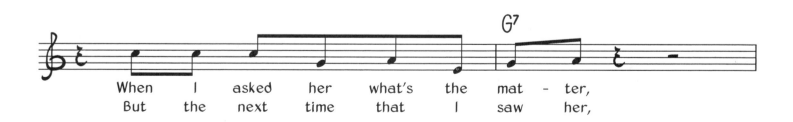

this is what I heard her say.)
re-mind-ed her of what she said.)

See you la - ter, Al - li - ga - tor;

in a while, Croc - o - dile._____

See you la - ter, Al - li - ga - tor;

in a while, Croc - o - - dile,_____

Can't you see you're in my way, now?

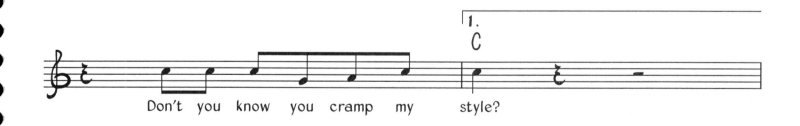

Don't you know you cramp my style?

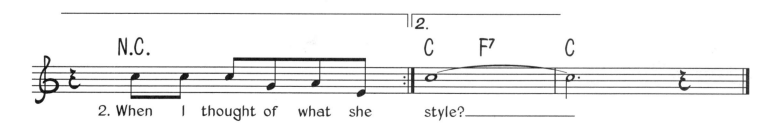

2. When I thought of what she style?_____

243

Shake, Rattle And Roll

(Rock 'N' Roll)

Words & Music by Charles Calhoun

Get out___ o' that kitch-en and rat-tle those pots and pans!___

Get out___ o' that kitch-en and rat-tle those pots and pans!___

Well, roll my break-fast, 'cause I'm a hun-gry man!___

Shake, rat-tle and roll!___ Shake, rat-tle and roll!___

Shake, rat-tle and roll!___ Shake, rat-tle and roll!___

You nev-er do noth-in' to save your dog-gone soul!___

She Was One Of The Early Birds
(Old-Time Waltz)

Words & Music by T.W. Connor

She was a dear lit-tle dick—ey bird,

"Chip! Chip! Chip!" she went;_____

Sweet——ly she sang to me till

all my mo-ney was spent._____ Then she

went off song._____ We

part-ed on fight——ing terms,_____

She was one of the ear——ly birds, And

I was one of the worms._____

She Wore A Yellow Ribbon

(Old-Time)

Traditional

Round her neck she wore a yel - low rib - bon, She

wore it in the spring - time and in the month of May. And

if you asked her why the heck she wore it, She

said "It's for my lov - er who is far, far a - way." Far a -

- way,_____ far a - way,_____ She

wore it for her lov - er far a - way._____

Round her neck she wore a yel - low rib - bon, She

wore it for her lov - er who was far, far a - way.

St. Bernard Waltz
(Old-Time)

Words by H.O. Ward ★ Music by Doug Swallow

Softly, Softly

(Waltz)

Words & Music by Paddy Roberts, Pierre Dudan & Mark Paul

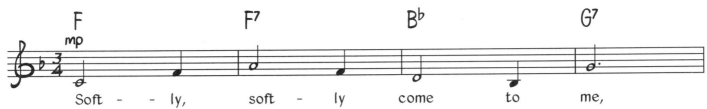

Soft - - ly, soft - ly come to me,

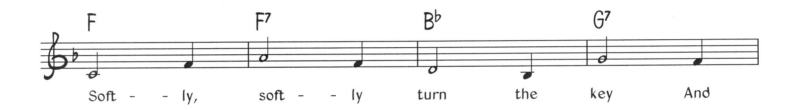

Touch my lips so ten - - der - ly.

Soft - - ly, soft - - ly turn the key And

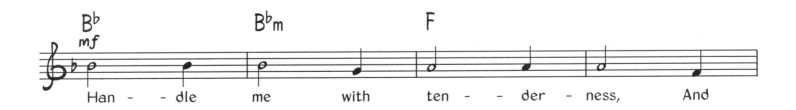

o - - pen up my heart._____

Han - - dle me with ten - - der - ness, And

say you'll leave me nev - - er.

In the warmth of your ca - ress, My

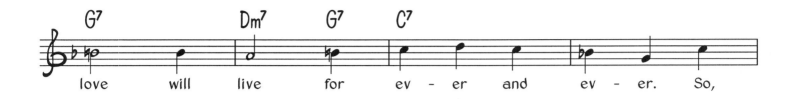

love will live for ev - er and ev - er. So,

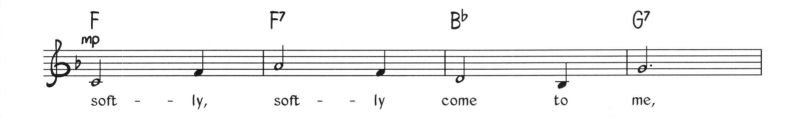

soft - - ly, soft - - ly come to me,

Touch my lips so ten - - der - ly.

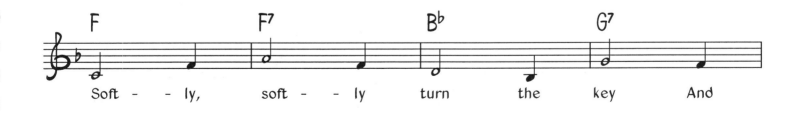

Soft - - ly, soft - - ly turn the key And

o - - pen up my heart._____

The Spinning Wheel
(Irish Waltz)

Words & Music by John Francis Waller & Delia Murphy

1. Mel - low, the moon - light to shine is be - gin - ning._____
2. "Eil - een, a ca - ra, I hear some - one tap - ping." "'Tis the
(Verses 3, 4, 5, 6, 7 see block lyric)

Close by the win - dow, young Eil - een is spin - ning.
i - vy, dear mo - ther, a - gainst the glass flap - ping."

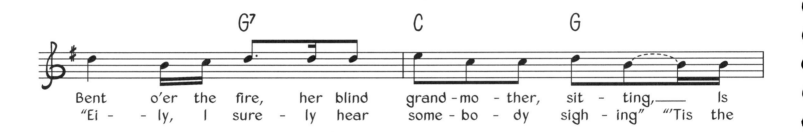

Bent o'er the fire, her blind grand - mo - ther, sit - ting,_____ Is
"Ei - - ly, I sure - ly hear some - bo - dy sigh - ing" "'Tis the

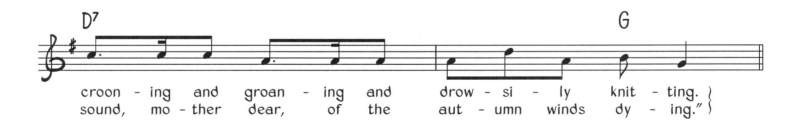

croon - ing and groan - ing and drow - si - ly knit - ting. }
sound, mo - ther dear, of the au - tumn winds dy - ing." }

Mer - ri - ly, cheer - i - ly, nois - i - ly whir - ring,

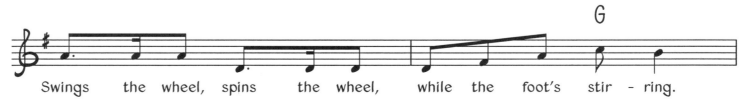

Swings the wheel, spins the wheel, while the foot's stir - ring.

Spright - ly and light - ly and air - i - ly ring -ing, Sounds the sweet voice of the

young maid - en sing -ing.

3. What's that
4. There's a
5. The

Verse 3
"What's that noise that I hear at the window, I wonder?"
"'Tis the little birds chirping the holly-bush under."
"What makes you be pushing and moving your stool on,
And singing all wrong that old song of Coolin?"

Verse 4
There's a form at the casement, the form of her true love,
And he whispers with face bent "I'm waiting for you, love.
Get up on the stool, through the lattice step lightly,
And we'll rove the grove while the moon's shining brightly."

Verse 5
The maid shakes her head, on her lips lays her fingers,
Steals up from the seat, longs to go and yet lingers;
A frightened glance turns to her drowsy grandmother,
Puts one foot on the stool, spins the wheel with the other.

Verse 6
Lazily, easily, swings now the wheel round,
Slowly and lowly is heard now the reel's sound.
Noiseless and light, to the lattice above her
The maid steps, then leaps to the arms of her lover.

Verse 7
Slower and slower and slower the wheel swings,
Lower and lower and lower the reel rings.
'Ere the reel and the wheel stop their spinning and moving,
Through the grove the young lovers by moonlight are roving.

Stormy Weather
(Slow Foxtrot)

Words by Ted Koehler ★ Music by Harold Arlen

Don't know why_____ there's no sun up in the sky, stor - my

weath - er;_____ since my gal and I_____ ain't to geth - er,_____

Keeps rain - in' all___ the time._____ Life is

bare,_____ gloom and mis - 'ry ev - 'ry - where, stor - my weath -er;_____

Just can't get my poor___ self to -geth -er,_____ I'm wea -ry all___ the

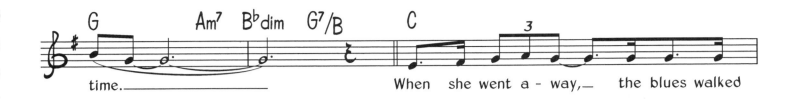

time._____ When she went a-way,___ the blues walked

in and met me; If she stays a-way,___ old rock-in' chair will get me.

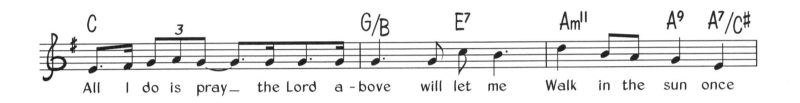

All I do is pray___ the Lord a-bove will let me Walk in the sun once

more. Can't go on,_____ ev-'ry-thing I had is gone, stor-my

weath-er;___ Since my girl and I___ ain't to-geth-er,___

Keeps rain-in' all___ the time._____

253

Suddenly You Love Me
(Quickstep)

Original Words & Music by D. Pace, M. Panzeri & L. Pilat ★ English Words by Peter Callander

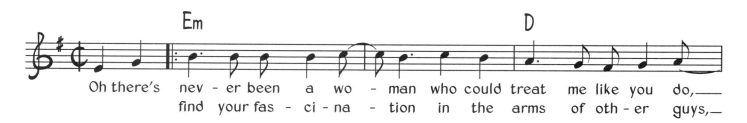

Oh there's nev - er been a wo - man who could treat me like you do,___
find your fas - ci - na - tion in the arms of oth - er guys,___

___ who could tram - ple on my pride___ and play a - round as much as you.___
___ you must know my re - pu - ta - tion comes to no - thing in their eyes.___

___ Well you real - ly shake my mind___ up with your cheat - ing and your lies,___
___ Still you take off in a hur - ry an - y -time it pleas-es you___

___ till at last I make my mind___ up and I turn___ to say good - bye,___
___ and you on - ly start to wor - ry when I say___ I'm leav-ing you,___

___ say good - bye._____
___ leav - ing you._____

Sud - den-ly you love___ me and your arms are o-pen wide,___

sud - den-ly there's no - thing that could tear you from my side.___

Ev - 'ry time it hap - pens as I turn to walk a-way,___

Sud - den-ly you love___ me and I know I got-ta stay.___ Zai zai zai

zai   Zai zai zai zai   Zai zai zai

zai   Zai zai zai zai   When you

Sugarbush
(Novelty Quickstep)

Words & Music by Josef Marais

1. Sug - ar - bush, come dance with me,
2. Choc - o - late, you are so sweet,

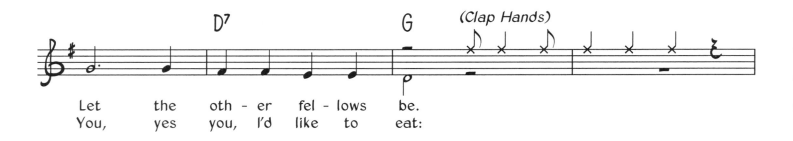

Let the oth - er fel - lows be.
You, yes you, I'd like to eat:

Dance the Pol - ka mer - ri - ly,
If I do, oh, what a treat!

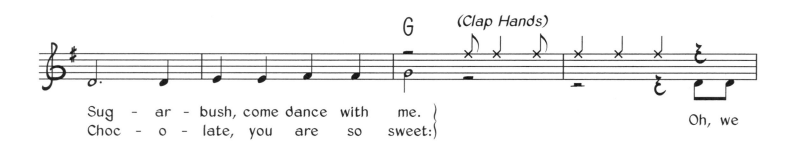

Sug - ar - bush, come dance with me. }
Choc - o - late, you are so sweet: }

Oh, we

nev - er not gon - na go home! We won't go, we won't go! Oh, we

nev - er not gon - na go phone, 'Cause mo - ther is - n't home! { Oh, { Oh,

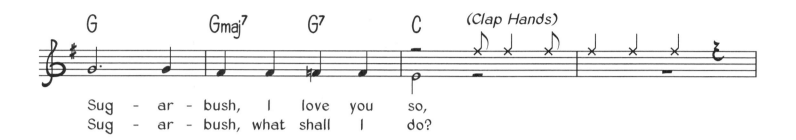

Sug - ar - bush, I love you so,
Sug - ar - bush, what shall I do?

I will nev - er let you go.
Mo - ther's not so pleased with you.

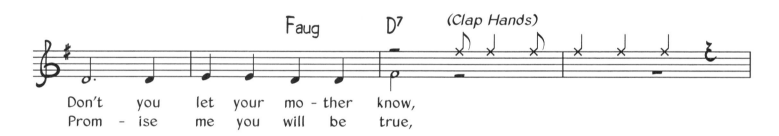

Don't you let your mo - ther know,
Prom - ise me you will be true,

1.
Sug - ar - bush, I love you so.
And I'll come a - long with

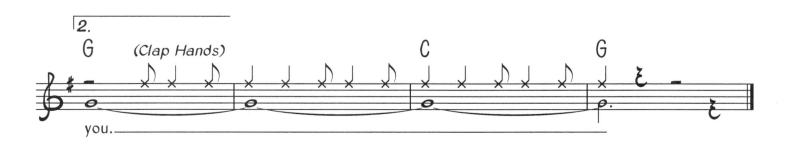

2.
you._____

Swedish Rhapsody (Midsummer Vigil)
(Polka)

Based on themes by Hugo Alfvén ★ Adaptation by Percy Faith

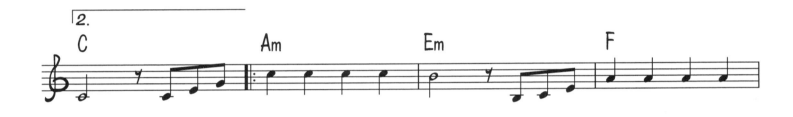

259

Sweet Little Sixteen

(Rock 'N' Roll)

Words & Music by Chuck Berry

They're real-ly rock-in' in Bos - ton_ in Pitts-burgh P. A.,

Deep in the heart of Tex - as, and round the Fris - co_ Bay._

All ov - er St. Lou - is, way down in New Or - leans,_

All the cats wan - na dance with_ sweet lit-tle six - teen._

Sweet lit-tle six - teen,_ she's just got to have_

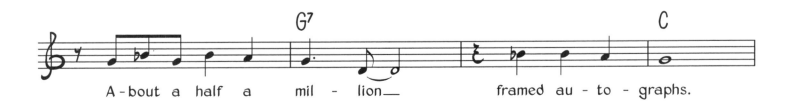

A-bout a half a mil - lion_ framed au - to - graphs.

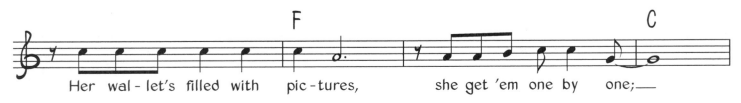

Her wal - let's filled with pic - tures, she get 'em one by one;_

Be-comes so ex - cit - ed,__ watch her, look at her run.__

Oh Mom - my, Mom - my,_____ please may I go?

It's such a sight to see__ some - bo - dy steal the show.__

Oh Dad - dy Dad - dy,_____ I beg of you, Whis - per_ to

D. S. al Coda

Mom - my__ it's all right with you. They're real-ly rock-in' in

CODA

All the cats wan-na dance with_ sweet lit-tle six - teen.__

Sweet Genevieve
(Old-Time Slow Waltz)

Words by George Cooper ★ Music by Henry Tucker

O Ge - ne - vieve, I'd give the world To live a - gain the

love - ly past! The rose of youth is dew - im - pearl'd, But now it with - ers

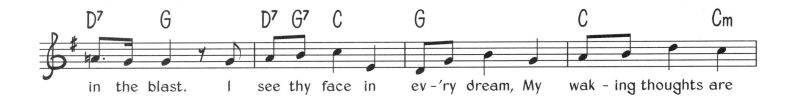

in the blast. I see thy face in ev - 'ry dream, My wak - ing thoughts are

full of thee, Thy glance is in the star - ry beam That falls a - long the

sum - mer sea!__ O Ge - ne - vieve, Sweet Ge - ne - vieve, The

days may come, the days__ may go, But still the hands of

mem - 'ry weave The bliss - ful dreams of long a - go.

Ta-Ra-Ra Boom De-Ay

(Old-Time)

Words & Music by Henry J. Sayers

Ta - ra - ra Boom - de - ay, Ta - ra - ra

Boom de - ay, Ta - ra - ra Boom - de - ay,

Ta - ra - ra Boom - de - ay. Ta - ra - ra

Boom - de - ay, Ta - ra - ra Boom - de - ay, Ta - ra - ra

Boom - de - ay, Ta - ra - ra Boom - de - ay.

That'll Be The Day
(Rock 'N' Roll)

Words & Music by Buddy Holly, Norman Petty & Jerry Allison

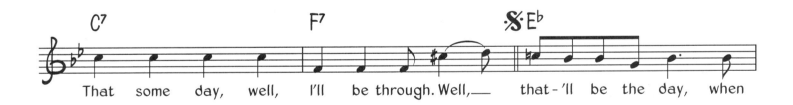

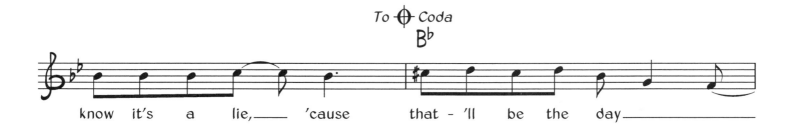

know it's a lie,_____ 'cause that - 'll be the day_____

____ when I die.____ Well, when Cu - pid shot his dart,

He shot it at your heart, So if we ev - er part and

I leave you, You say you told me an' you

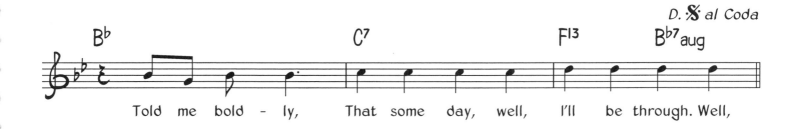

Told me bold - ly, That some day, well, I'll be through. Well,

that - 'll be the day,_____ when I die.____

Thoroughly Modern Millie
(Quickstep)

Words by Sammy Cahn ★ Music by James Van Heusen

Ev - 'ry - thing to - day is tho - rough - ly mod - ern.—
Ev - 'ry - thing to - day is tho - rough - ly mod - ern.—

(Check your per - so - na - li - ty) Ev - 'ry - thing to - day makes yes - ter - day
(Brands are get - ting jaz - zi - er) Ev - 'ry - thing to - day is start - ing to

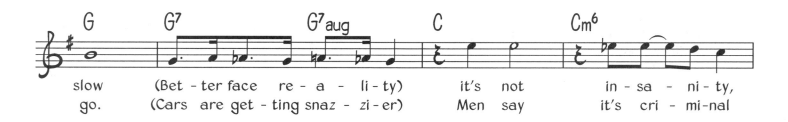

slow (Bet - ter face re - a - li - ty) it's not in - sa - ni - ty,
go. (Cars are get - ting snaz - zi - er) Men say it's cri - mi - nal

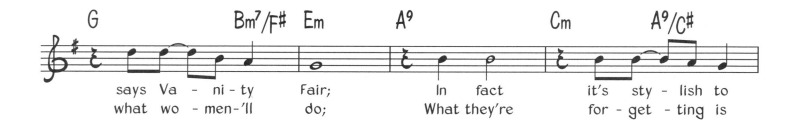

says Va - ni - ty Fair; In fact it's sty - lish to
what wo - men - 'll do; What they're for - get - ting is

raise your skirts and bob your hair! (Instr.)
this is nine - teen twen - ty - two!— (Instr.)

In a rum - ble seat, the world is so co - sy,___
Have you seen the way they kiss___ in the mov - ies?___

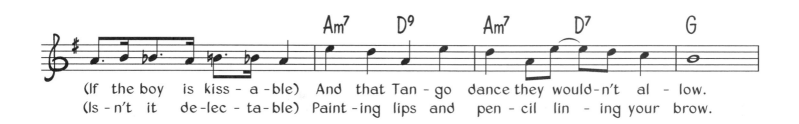

(If the boy is kiss - a -ble) And that Tan - go dance they would-n't al - low.
(Is - n't it de -lec - ta -ble) Paint -ing lips and pen - cil lin - ing your brow.

(Now is quite per - mis - sa -ble)
(Now is quite re -spect a -ble)   Good -bye,   good-good -y girl;   I'm chang -ing, and

how!   So beat the drums, 'cause here comes Tho - rough-ly Mod - ern

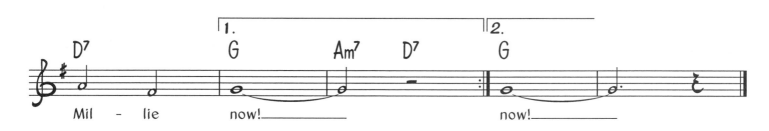

Mil - lie   now!_____   now!_____

Those Lazy Hazy Crazy Days Of Summer

(Quickstep)

Original Words & Music by Hans Carste & Hans Bradtke ★ English Words by Charles Tobias

Roll out those la - zy ha - zy cra - zy days of

sum - mer, Those days of so - da and pret - zels and

beer. Roll out those la - zy ha - zy cra - zy days of

sum - mer; Dust off the sun and moon and sing a song of

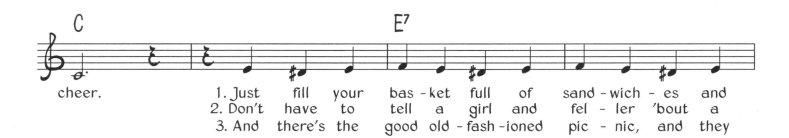

cheer.

1. Just fill your bas - ket full of sand - wich - es and
2. Don't have to tell a girl and fel - ler 'bout a
3. And there's the good old - fash - ioned pic - nic, and they

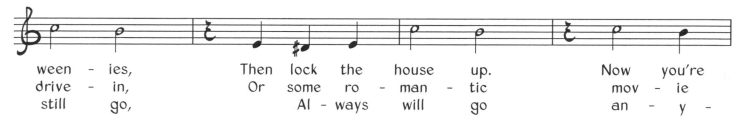

ween - ies, Then lock the house up. Now you're
drive - in, Or some ro - man - tic mov - ie
still go, Al - ways will go an - y -

That's The Way (I Like It)
(Medium Disco)

Words & Music by Harry Casey & Richard Finch

Ooh_____ Ooh_____

Ooh_____ Ooh_____

That's the way (uh huh uh huh) I like it, (uh huh uh huh)

That's the way, (uh huh uh huh) I like it, (uh huh uh huh).

That's the way, (uh huh uh huh) I like it, (uh huh uh huh).

Fine

That's the way, (uh huh uh huh) I like it, (uh huh uh huh).

1. Will you take_ me by the hand_ and tell me I'm__ your lov-ing
2. Will I get_ to be in your arms_ with my arms_ all a-

man? will you give me all your love and
- round. Will you whis - per sweet in my ears,

D.C. al Fine

do it babe,_ the ve-ry best you can? Oh
will you turn,_ turn me on. Oh

A Time For Us
(Love Theme from 'Romeo & Juliet')
(Slow Waltz)

Words by Eddie Snyder & Larry Kusik ★ Music by Nino Rota

Too-Ra-Loo-Ra-Loo-Ral
(That's An Irish Lullaby)
(Irish Waltz)

Words & Music by J.R. Shannon

1. Ov - er in Kil - lar - ney,_____ ma - ny years a -
2. Oft in dreams I wan - der_____ to that cot a -

- go,_____ Me mith - er sang a song to me in
- gain,_____ I feel her arms a - hug - ging me as

tones so sweet and low:_____ Just a sim - ple lit - tle
when she held me then;_____ And I hear her voice a -

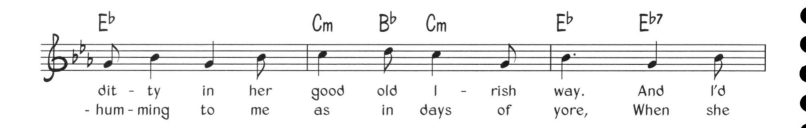

dit - ty in her good old I - rish way. And I'd
- hum - ming to me as in days of yore, When she

give the world if she could sing that song to me to -
used to rock me fast a - sleep out - side the cab - in

- day._____ }
door._____ } " Too - ra - loo - ra - loo - ral,_____

Too - ra - loo - ra - li. Too - ra - loo - ra -

- loo - ral,_____ Hush now, don't you cry!_____

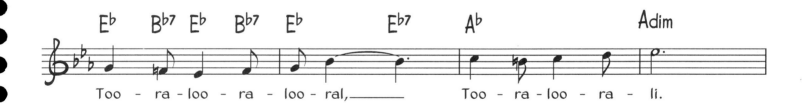

Too - ra - loo - ra - loo - ral,_____ Too - ra - loo - ra - li.

Too - ra - loo - ra - loo - ral, That's an I - rish lul - la -

- by. -loo - ral, That's an I - rish lul - la - by._____

Tutti Frutti
(Rock 'N' Roll)

Words & Music by Richard Penniman, Dorothy La Bostrie & Joe Lubin

A - bop - bop - a - loom - op a - lop bop boom! Tut - ti Frut - ti au

rut - ti, Tut - ti Frut - ti au rut - ti, Tut - ti

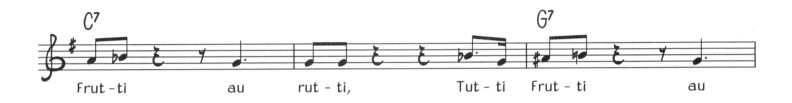

Frut - ti au rut - ti, Tut - ti Frut - ti au

rut - ti, Tut - ti Frut - ti au rut - ti, A -

- bop - bop a - loom - op a lop bop boom! I got a gal, her name's
gal, her name's

Sue, She knows just what to do____ I got a
Dai - sy, She al - most drives me cra - - zy, I got a

gal,   her name's Sue   She knows just what to do__
gal,   her name's Dai - sy,   She al - most drives me cra -

—   zy   I've been   to the east,   I've been   to the west,   But
— zy   She's a   real   gone__ cook - ie,   yes - sir - ree,   But

she's   the   gal__   I   love   the   best.__ } Tut - ti   Frut - ti   au
pret - ty lit - tle   Su - zy's   the   gal   for me.__

rut - ti,   Tut - ti   Frut - ti   au   rut - ti,   Tut - ti

Frut - ti   au   rut - ti,   Tut - ti   Frut - ti   au

rut - ti,   Tut - ti   Frut - ti   au   rut - ti,   A -

- bop - bop a - loom - op   a - lop   bop boom!   I got a   lop bop boom!

Tragedy
(Medium Disco)

Words & Music by Barry Gibb, Robin Gibb & Maurice Gibb

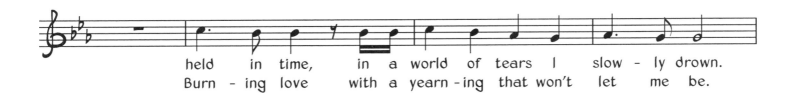

Here I lie in a lost and lone-ly part of town,
Night and day there's a burn-ing down in-side of me,

held in time, in a world of tears I slow-ly drown.
Burn-ing love with a yearn-ing that won't let me be.

Go - in' home I just can't make it all a-lone, I
Down I go and I just can't take it all a-lone, I

real-ly should be hold-ing you, hold-ing you, lov-ing you,
real-ly should be hold-ing you, hold-ing you, lov-ing you,

lov - ing you._____
lov - ing you._____

Tra-ge-dy,— when the

feel-ing's gone and you can't go on, it's tra-ge-dy;— when the

morn - ing cries and you don't know why, it's hard to bear— with

no one to love you you're go - in' no - where.

Tra - ge - dy,— when you lose con - trol and you got no soul, it's

tra - ge - dy;— when the morn-ing cries and you don't know why, it's

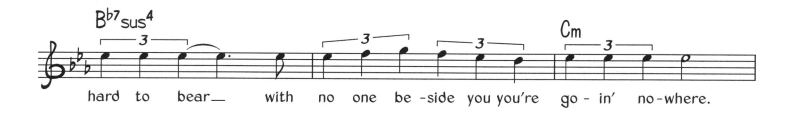

hard to bear— with no one be -side you you're go - in' no-where.

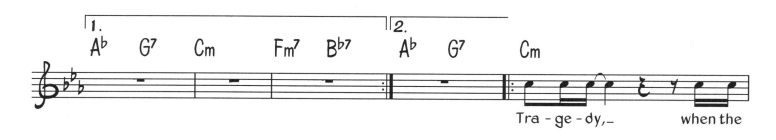

Tra - ge - dy,— when the

Gm   Cm

feel - ing's gone and you can't go on, it's tra - ge - dy;—   when the

Gm $B^{b7}sus^4$

morn - ing cries and you don't know why, it's hard to bear— with

                     Cm A^b G^7

no one to love you, you're go - in' no - where.

Cm   Gm

Tra - ge - dy,—   when you lose con - trol and you got no soul, it's

Cm   Gm

tra - ge - dy;—   when the morn - ing cries and your heart just dies, it's

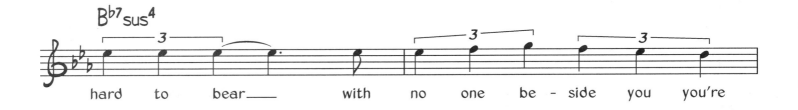

$B^{b7}sus^4$

hard to bear—— with no one be - side you you're

┌ Optional number ┐┌ Last time ┐

Cm A^b G   Cm

go - in' no - where.   Oh.——

Use It Up And Wear It Out
(Medium Disco)

Words & Music by Lawrence Brown & Sandy Linzer

Ev-'ry-bo-dy, all you peo-ple ga-ther round, and let your bo-dy mu-sic move it up and move it down. We're gon-na use it up, gon-na wear it out, ain't noth-in' left in this whole world I care a-bout. I said one, two, three, shake your bo-dy down, one, two, three, shake your bo-dy down to me.__ One, two, three, shake your bo-dy down. One, two, three, oh shake your_____ bo-dy_____ down._____ Gon-na use it up, gon-na wear it out. Ain't no-thin' left in this whole world I

Optional number

care a-bout.

Last time

I said care a-bout. Gon-na use it up!

Welcome Home (Vivre)
(Foxtrot)

French Words by Jean Dupre ★ Music by Stanislas Beldone ★ English Words by Bryan Blackburn

I'm so a - lone my love with - out__ you,__

You're part of ev - 'ry - thing__ I__ do.

When you_ come back,_____ and you're be - side__ me,_

These are_ the words I'll say to you:_____

Chorus

Wel - - come home, wel - - come;

Come on in and close the door.

When I Need You
(Waltz)

Words & Music by Albert Hammond & Carole Bayer Sager

When I ___ need you, I just close my eyes and I'm

(Verse 3 see block lyric)

with you, and all that I so want to give you is

on - ly a heart-beat a - way. ___ When I

need love, I hold out my hands and I touch

love; I nev - er knew there was so much love, it's

keep - ing me warm night and day. ___

Miles and miles of emp - ty space in be - tween ___ us; ___ the

te - le - phone can't take the place of your smile. ___ But you

know I won't be tra-vel-ling for ev - er; it's cold out, but

1.
hold out and do like I do.— 2. When I do like I do.— Oh, I

need— you. *Instrumental*

3. When I

Verse 2
When I need you,
I just close my eyes and I'm with you,
And all that I so want to give you, baby,
Is only a heartbeat away.
It's not easy when the road is your driver;
But, honey, that's a heavy load that we bear.
But you know I won't be travelling a lifetime;
It's cold out, but hold out and do like I do.
Oh, I need you.

Verse 3
When I need love,
I hold out my hands and I touch love.
I never knew there was so much love,
It's keeping me warm night and day.
I just hold out my hand,
I just hold out my hand
And I'm with you, darling... *(etc. ad lib.)*

When Irish Eyes Are Smiling
(Irish Waltz)

Words by George Graff & Chauncey Olcott ★ Music by Ernest Ball

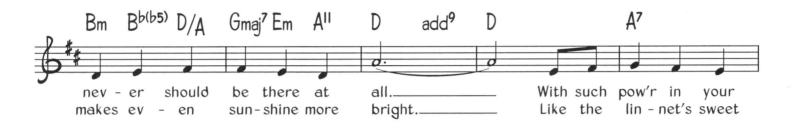

Where Will The Dimple Be?

(Quickstep)

Words & Music by Bob Merrill & Al Hoffman

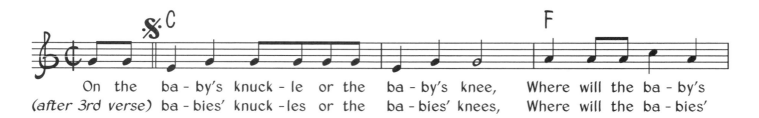

On the ba - by's knuck - le or the ba - by's knee, Where will the ba - by's
(after 3rd verse) ba - bies' knuck - les or the ba - bies' knees, Where will the ba - bies'

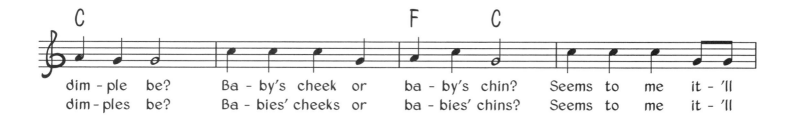

dim - ple be? Ba - by's cheek or ba - by's chin? Seems to me it - 'll
dim - ples be? Ba - bies' cheeks or ba - bies' chins? Seems to me it - 'll

be a sin if it's al - ways co - vered by a safe - ty pin. Where will the dim - ple
be a sin if they're al - ways co - vered by a safe - ty pin. Where will the dim - ples

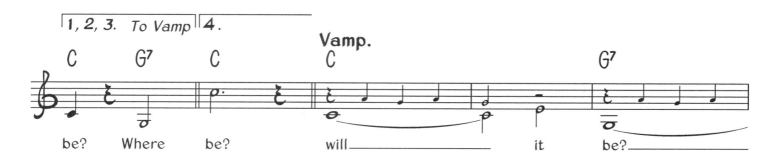

1, 2, 3. To Vamp | 4.

Vamp.

be? Where be? will   it be?

Verses

1. Ev - 'ry night we stay at home, my love and me a - lone, mak - in'
— (Verses 2, 3 see block lyric)

wish - es ov - er dish - es in the sink. Will our

bun - dle - full of joy Be a dar - lin' girl or boy, Will the

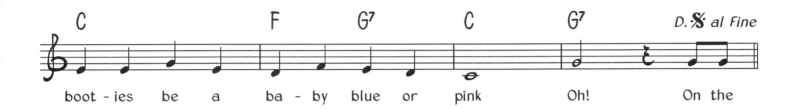

boot - ies be a ba - by blue or pink Oh! On the

Verse 2
Now I wake up ev'ry night with such an appetite,
Eat a choc'late pie topped off with saurkraut.
Then I put some records on, munch on crackers until dawn,
And just sit around all night and try to guess.
Oh! On the baby's knuckles or the baby's knee,
Where will the baby's dimple be?
Baby's cheek or baby's chin?
Seems to me it'll be a sin if it's always covered by a safety pin.
Where will the dimple be?

Verse 3
While I play the clingin' vine, I watch that love of mine
Buildin' cradles while I'm peckin' at his cheek.
Not just one, but two or three; twins run in my family,
And my cousin Jane had triplets just last week.
Oh! On the babies' knuckles or the babies' knees,
Where will the babies' dimples be?
Babies' cheeks or babies' chins?
Seems to me it'll be a sin if they're always covered by a safety pin.
Where will the dimples be?

We Are Family
(Medium Disco)

Words & Music by Bernard Edwards & Nile Rodgers

While Strolling Through The Park One Day

(Old-Time)

Words & Music by Ed Haley & Robert A. Keiser

Wives And Lovers
(Waltz)

Words by Hal David ★ Music by Burt Bacharach

A White Sport Coat And A Pink Carnation

(Quickstep)

Words & Music by Marty Robbins

A white sport coat and a pink car-na-tion, I'm all dressed up for the dance,___ A white sport coat and a pink car-na-tion, I'm all a-lone in ro-mance.___

Once you told me long a-go,___ To the prom with me you'd go,___ Now you've changed your mind it seems,___ Some-one else will hold my dreams. A white sport coat and a pink car-na-tion, I'm in a blue, blue mood.___

Wonderful Copenhagen
(Waltz)

Words & Music by Frank Loesser

Won - der - ful, won - der - ful Co - pen - ha - gen,
Won - der - ful, won - der - ful Co - pen - ha - gen,

friend - ly old girl of a town,_____ 'neath her
sal - ty old queen of the sea._____ Once I

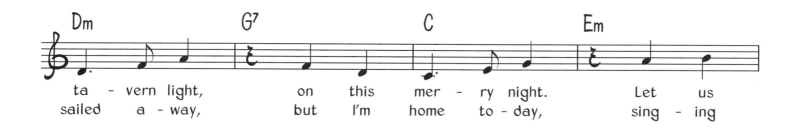

ta - vern light, on this mer - ry night. Let us
sailed a - way, but I'm home to - day, sing - ing

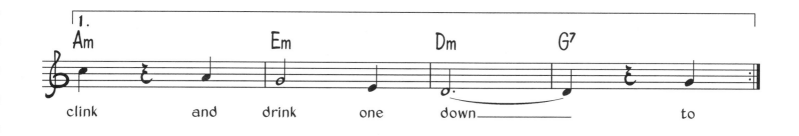

1.

clink and drink one down_____ to

2.

Co - pen - ha - gen, won - der - ful, won - der - ful

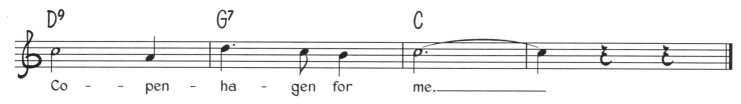

Co - pen - ha - gen for me._____

293

You Brought A New Kind Of Love To Me

(Foxtrot)

Words & Music by Sammy Fain, Irving Kahal & Pierre Norman

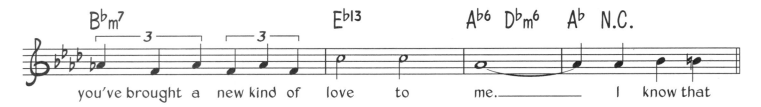

I'm the slave, you're the queen, But still you can un- -der-

-stand__ That, un-der-neath it all, you're a maid And I am on- -ly a

man. I would work and slave_ the whole day through,__ If

I could hur- -ry home to you;__ For you've brought a new kind of

love to me._____ If the me._____

You Light Up My Life
(Waltz)

Words & Music by Joe Brooks

So ma - ny nights   I'd sit by my win - dow,
Rol - lin' at sea,   a - drift on the wa - ters,

Wait - ing for some - one___ to sing me his song.
Could it be fi - n'lly___ I'm turn - ing for home?

So ma - ny dreams   I kept deep in - side me,   A -
Fi - n'lly a chance to say, "Hey! I love you."

- lone in the dark, But now you've come a - long.)   And
Nev - er a - gain to___ be all a - lone.)

you light up my life, You give me

hope to car - ry on. You light up my

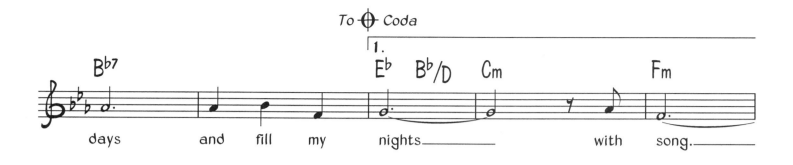

To ⊕ Coda

1.

Bb7 · · · Eb Bb/D Cm Fm

days and fill my nights_____ with song._____

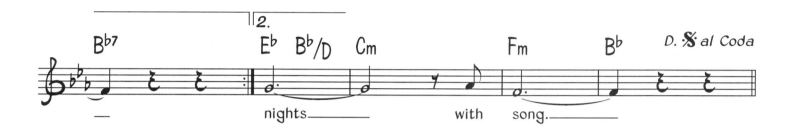

2.

Bb7 Eb Bb/D Cm Fm Bb D. 𝄋 al Coda

— nights_____ with song._____

⊕ CODA

G Cm F9 Eb/Bb

nights with song. It can't be wrong_____ when

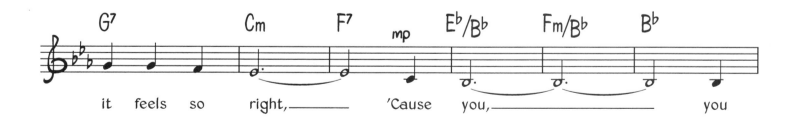

G7 Cm F7 mp Eb/Bb Fm/Bb Bb

it feels so right,_____ 'Cause you,_____ you

Ab Eb/Bb Bb Ab Eb/G Fm7 Eb

light up my life._____

Young At Heart
(Slow Foxtrot)

Words by Carolyn Leigh ★ Music by Johnny Richards

Fair - y tales— can come true,— it can hap-pen to you if you're
know— that it's worth— ev -'ry trea-sure on earth to be

young at heart.— For it's hard,— you will find,— to be
young at heart.— For as rich— as you are,— it's much

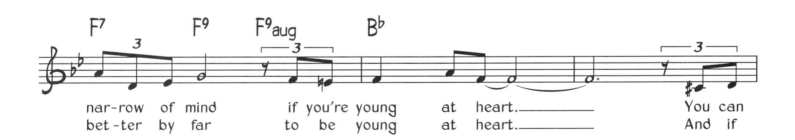

nar-row of mind if you're young at heart.— You can
bet -ter by far to be young at heart.— And if

go— to ex - tremes— with im - pos - si - ble schemes, You can
you— should sur - vive to a hun - dred and five, Look at

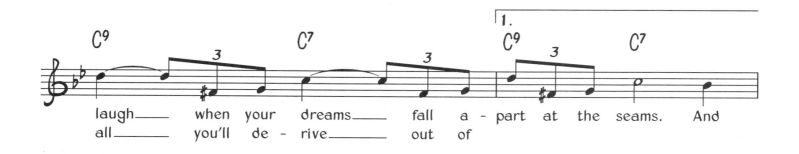

laugh____ when your dreams____ fall a - part at the seams. And
all____ you'll de - rive____ out of

life gets more ex - ci - ting with each pass - ing day,____ And

love is ei - ther in your heart or on the way.____ Don't you

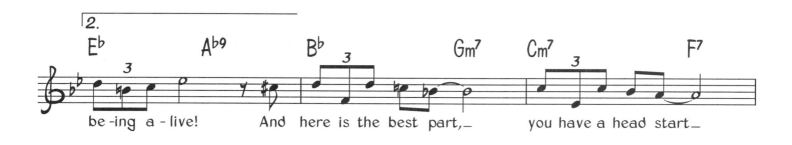

be -ing a - live! And here is the best part,_ you have a head start_

If you are a - mong the ve - ry young at heart._

Young Hearts Run Free
(Medium Disco)

Words & Music by David Crawford

What's the sense in shar-ing this one and on-ly life,

end - ing up just an - oth - er lost and lone - ly wife.

You count up the years and they will___ be filled with tears.

Love on - ly breaks up to start ov - er a -gain. And

you'll get the ba - bies but you won't have your man.

While he is bu - sy lov - ing ev - e-ry wo - man that he can.

Say I'm gon-na leave a hun-dred times a day, it's

ea-si-er said than done, when you just can't break a-way,

just can't break a-way. Young hearts, run free, nev-er be hung up,

hung up like my man and me, my man and me.

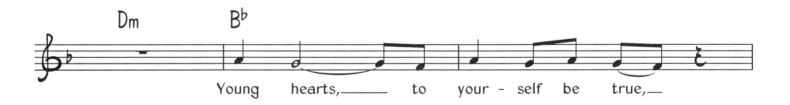

Young hearts, to your-self be true,

don't be no fool when love real-ly don't love you,

don't love you.

You're Nobody 'Til Somebody Loves You

(Quickstep)

Words & Music by Russ Morgan, Larry Stock & James Cavanaugh

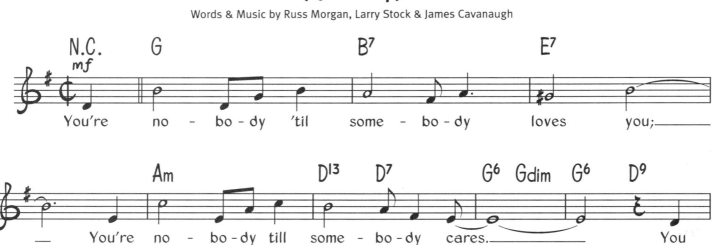

You're no - bo - dy 'til some - bo - dy loves you;

You're no - bo - dy till some - bo - dy cares. You

may be king, you may pos - sess the world and its gold, But

gold won't bring you hap - pi - ness when you're grow - ing old. The

world still is the same, you'll nev - er change it, As

sure as the stars shine a - bove. You're

no - bo - dy 'til some - bo - dy loves you, So

find your - self some - bo - dy to love.

Get real...
Play the world's greatest music instantly
with these bumper collections of jazz and blues numbers,
and all-time great songs.

Easy-to-read melody line arrangements by Jack Long, with chord symbols and lyrics (where appropriate).

The Real Book of **Jazz**

Over 190 great jazz standards including...
A Foggy Day; Ain't Misbehavin'; April In Paris;
Caravan; Crazy Rhythm; Django; Don't Blame Me;
Fascinating Rhythm; Fly Me To The Moon; Frenesi;
Honeysuckle Rose; I'm Beginning To See The Light;
In The Still Of The Night; Just One Of Those Things;
Lullaby Of Birdland; Night Flight; Oh, Lady, Be Good;
Opus One; Perdido; Petite Fleur; Satin Doll; So Nice;
Splanky; Straight No Chaser; That Old Black Magic;
Waltz For Debbie; Wave and Who's Sorry Now?

Order No. AM952435

The Real Book of **Blues**

225 big blues numbers including...
After You've Gone; All Or Nothing At All; Black Coffee;
Blues Stay Away From Me; Bluesette; Body And Soul;
Chelsea Bridge; Crazy Man Blues; Dust My Broom;
Fever; Frankie And Johnny; Georgia On My Mind;
Here's That Rainy Day; How Insensitive; If I Had You;
Lazybones; Li'l Darlin'; Memphis Blues; Misty;
Moonglow; More Than You Know; Singing The Blues;
Solitude; Sunny; Take These Chains From My Heart;
When Sunny Gets Blue and Worried Man Blues.

Order No. AM952446

The Real Book of
Great Songs

Over 200 all-time great songs including...
A Fine Romance; A Woman In Love; Amapola;
Arrivederci Roma; Be Mine Tonight; Carolina Moon;
Climb Ev'ry Mountain; Delicado; El Cumbanchero;
Fools Rush In; For All We Know; Getting To Know You;
I Left My Heart In San Francisco; London By Night;
Memories Are Made Of This; My Favourite Things;
Oklahoma; Paper Roses; Raindrops Keep Falling On
My Head; She; Spanish Eyes; Strangers In The Night;
The Folks Who Live On The Hill; The Twelfth Of Never;
This Guy's In Love With You; Tonight; Too Young;
Unchained Melody; Unforgettable; Vaya Con Dios;
What Kind Of Fool Am I; Whispering Grass and
Yesterday When I Was Young.

Order No. AM952468